420

R & D Administration

R & D Administration

G. Stuart Monteith, B.Sc., C.Eng., M.I.E.E.,
M.Inst.P., M.B.I.M.

Ministry of Technology

LONDON   ILIFFE BOOKS LTD

ILIFFE BOOKS LTD
42 RUSSELL SQUARE
LONDON, W.C.1

First published in 1969

© *G. Stuart Monteith* 1969

592   03511   5

Filmset by Photoprint Plates Ltd,
Wickford, Essex
Printed in England by
J. W. Arrowsmith Ltd, Bristol

Contents

Preface

Research and development must include the planning and administration of the work as well as the actual performance. Because this type of work is one of the least predictable of human activities, its planning and administration poses unique problems, the investigation of which has given rise to a new discipline—research on research.

The aim of this book is to define the problems and give answers based on present practices, with the intention that the reader will criticise those methods in current use by himself. As problems are delineated by facts, the facts considered relevant to R & D administration, in particular the law relating to patents and contracts, and also accountancy methods, are included. To prevent the book from being parochial, both United Kingdom and United States practices are given where these differ.

It is therefore hoped that this book will be of use to the graduate as a textbook; to the practising manager in defining his problems and acting as a source book; and also to the British or American scientist who crosses the Atlantic.

The contents of this book are based on lectures given by the author at Portsmouth College of Technology, to qualified students taking the final year of the joint Ministry of Education and British Institute of Management Certificate in Management Studies. These lectures were subsequently tailored to meet the needs of the R & D worker, rather than the business executive, and appeared as a series in *British Communications and Electronics* under the generic title of 'Management Aspects of R & D'. In this book, these papers have been completely re-written and expanded to include the most recent practices.

The glossary is an exercise in semantics and may be criticised for inclusions and exclusions. The words have been selected on the basis either that they are technical terms that should be known, or that they are in common usage but have a special connotation in a particular context.

The author wishes to thank the directors and staff of the following companies, who have shown great interest in the book and have assisted in its preparation by helpful discussions, giving information on their own practices, and permitting the reproduction of certain forms:

Elliott Brothers (London) Limited
Louis Newmark Limited
The Plessey Company Limited
The Radio Corporation of America
Rotax Limited
Smiths Industries Limited
Ultra Electronics Limited

Special thanks are also due to the staff of the Central Library of the Ministry of Technology, who have assisted in obtaining books and reports, and to Brunel University for assistance in the preparation of the section on academic qualifications. Finally, the author wishes to thank Dr. A. D. I. Nicol of the School of Physical Science, University of Cambridge, and Chairman of the Education Group of the Institute of Physics, for reading and commenting on the manuscript.

The author is indebted to the Ministry of Technology for permission to write and publish this book, and attention is drawn to the fact that opinions expressed herein are not necessarily official.

Woking, 1969   G. S. M.

Foreword

HANDEL DAVIES, C.B.
Deputy Controller of Aircraft (Research and Development)
Ministry of Technology

It is no exaggeration to say that the problems which now confront those responsible for the administration of research and development are as difficult and complex as those arising from the scientific and practical aspects of the work. There is no shortage of ideas in the present day scientific and technical world. The real problem is to select at an early enough stage those ideas which are most likely to be capable of successful exploitation and then to organise the costly task of developing the idea through the successive phases of research and experiment to the ultimate commercial or military application, within a budget and a time limit.

The need to do this in the most efficient way possible is even more important for small countries like the United Kingdom, with limited resources in money and manpower and a small domestic market, than it is for the industrial giants like the United States. Yet it is the small countries which have been slow in establishing the techniques of management and administration which have become so necessary. The cost escalation and delays which have occurred in so many major projects in recent years, leading to the enforced abandonment of some of them, bears testimony to the inadequacy of many of our planning and management procedures. For the failures which have occurred have nearly all been due to inadequacies in initial planning, cost control, market research, and management techniques, rather than to any scientific or technical deficiencies.

There has, of course, been a widening recognition of this conclusion in recent years but much still remains to be done if the R & D foundations so necessary to future prospects are to be efficiently laid. What is needed is a more professional approach to the problem of R & D administration, and above all a recognition that the problems involved are in many ways fundamentally different from the more familiar ones usually found in industrial and commercial administration.

I believe this book will fulfil a great need, written as it is by one who has himself been actively engaged in R & D administration in one of the most difficult fields for many years.

Handel Davies

Chapter 1

Introduction

For an *activity* to be meaningful, the object of the activity must first be defined; that is, there must be a *policy statement*. *Planning* to achieve the objective will follow, and to put the plan into operation there must be an *organisational structure*, provided with the necessary funds and controlled so that it does not deviate from the objective.

The preparation of the policy statement and the plan to make it effective is commonly termed *direction*, whilst the executive action that follows is *administration*. Interwoven between these two functions is the art of *management*, by which is meant the handling of the personal relationships that arise.

Research and development (R & D) differs from most other business activities in that the plan will be formed largely from ideas originating within the group, and the outcome of the plan cannot be predicted accurately. This means that the research manager must be concerned in the direction of his work as well as the administration.

THE RANGE OF R & D ACTIVITY

Scientific research is defined in English Law[1] as 'any activities in the field of natural and applied science for the extension of knowledge'.

In the United States, R & D is stated[2] as being 'systematic and intensive study directed towards a fuller knowledge of the subject studied, and use of that knowledge directed towards the production of useful materials, devices, systems or processes.'

Scientists and engineers may categorise the subject more precisely in terms of five areas of work: pure basic research; objective basic research; applied research; development; and services.

PURE BASIC RESEARCH

Pure basic research has been described as the organised and systematic search for new principles and facts, with the object of:

1

(a) Learning and understanding the basic scientific laws which under-lie a particular phenomenon

(b) Learning and understanding the basic scientific laws which relate one or more particular phenomena to existing scientific knowledge.

OBJECTIVE BASIC RESEARCH

This is the detailed examination of:

(a) A particular phenomenon with the intent of establishing its technologically useful consequence

(b) A recognised technological requirement with the intent of finding within existing scientific knowledge, a way of satisfying such a requirement.

APPLIED RESEARCH

This is the creation of a practical proposition from an idea involving two stages: concept analysis and demonstration of concept.

(a) *Concept analysis*—the preliminary study of the consequences of an idea for creating a new, or improving an existing technique, product or equipment. There are three phases:
1. Analytical investigation of the practicality of the idea
2. Outlining the objectives and establishing a planned programme for accomplishing them
3. Preparing a specification for the techniques, product or equipment.

(b) *Demonstration of concept*—the preparation, by design, development and test activities, of a working laboratory model of the concept. This enables the potential of the technique, product or equipment to be demonstrated.

DEVELOPMENT

The design and engineering work necessary to take a project to the production stage falls into 3 phases, prototype design, production design and pilot manufacture.

(a) *Prototype design*—this involves making a prototype product or equipment, or demonstrating the technique. The following factors have to be established at this stage:
1. The basic method of manufacture and shape of the final product or equipment
2. Performance in accordance with the specification and market requirements

2

3. *Design approval* for release to production
4. *Type approval* where this is essential to the prime design concept.

(b) *Production design*—the re-design and styling of the prototype to meet manufacturing and/or market requirements; production tool design may be included.

(c) *Pilot manufacture* or *pre-production*—this will include:
1. Field testing
2. Elimination of production teething troubles
3. Obtaining type approval for the product or equipment.

SERVICES

(a) *Production*
1. Technical service to production
2. Compilation of service manuals, spares, schedules and catalogues
3. Licensor/licensee liaison
4. Minor experimental work
5. Maintenance of drawings.

(b) *Sales*
1. Technical service to sales
2. Service to customers, either at their own or the company's premises, to assist them to make the best possible use of the company's products or techniques
3. Investigation of faults and methods of application.

These areas of R & D work follow logically on each other and should be considered as a continuous spectrum rather than in isolation, the distinguishing parameter being increase in predictability.[3] Furthermore, there will be feedback to preceding areas, and the starting point in a cycle of work may occur anywhere within the spectrum. A classic example of this is the steam engine, which was developed before applied research modified it for traction; it was the need for improvement that gave rise to basic research on heat engines, properties of gases, and other subjects.

THE OBJECTIVES OF R & D

For R & D to exist, it must serve a purpose. For its continued existence, there must be an *incentive*.[4] In a university, it is generally acknowledged that the purpose of basic research is to contribute to human knowledge. It is not always appreciated that the incentive is sometimes the acclamation of the researcher's peers,[5] with perhaps the satisfaction of benefiting humanity.

These incentives may also apply to work in Government establishments, other than those concerned with Defence, which seek military

3

advantage. The chain of command in Government work, however, is necessarily of such a form that the researcher may not feel involved personally—a possible reason for the criticism sometimes made of the low productivity of Government R & D.

The aim of a technologically based company must be 'to create, make and market useful products and services to satisfy the need of its customers', whilst the incentive is the opportunity to make a profit. R & D cannot, therefore, be independent of *production* and *marketing*, but must co-operate with them in maintaining the company's position and creating new opportunities for profit making. These are the prime precepts of any company's policy. They can only be achieved by *innovation*, that is the concept of new ideas, originating from any of the three functions and successfully put into practice by their mutual co-operation; the effectiveness of the company as a whole is then demonstrated by it making a *profit*.[4]

A policy statement will amplify and define the precepts so as to give effective guidance to those responsible for planning the work. In military terms, the policy should be a declaration of the strategy, and the plan of work becomes the tactics by which the policy is achieved. This analogy highlights the need for good communications between the component parts of an organisation, while the utilisation of resources and good timing is also essential if the maximum gain is to be achieved.

As R & D is characterised by a low predictability, the strategy must be based on a sound choice of the tactics available, that is, the direction of research will affect policy. This is made clearer by considering the policy statement of an industrial organisation, which should give answers to questions such as:

(a) In what business does the company wish to engage
(b) What rate of growth is desired by the company
(c) What method of growth is intended, e.g. internal expansion, takeover
(d) What direction is growth intended to take—vertical or horizontal
(e) What is the desired technical image of the company
(f) What percentage of the market is sought by the company
(g) Which geographical markets are to be exploited
(h) What is the desired size of the company
(i) What are the possibilities of raising new capital
(j) What is the rate of return on capital.

The formulation of the answers will be dependent on the advice and forecasts submitted with regard to:

(a) The state of the art, and competitors' know-how
(b) Possible breakthroughs
(c) Patents and licenses
(d) Plans of work to implement the strategy, together with the probability of success
(e) Costs arising in implementing the strategy
(f) Results of successful strategies.

4

This advice may be considered as the feedback arising from the direction of research, but it will be weighted according to the assigned position of R & D within the organisation. This position will depend on the terms of reference given, which in turn must stem from the policy statement. In an industrial organisation these terms of reference must cover some, if not all, of the following objectives:

(a) To cure existing troubles and nuisances in connection with materials, processes, products and services, and to anticipate and prevent such trouble
(b) To reduce the costs involved in the use of materials, processes, products and services
(c) To improve the quality of existing materials, products and services
(d) To reduce the consumers' operating and maintenance costs
(e) To develop new uses for existing materials, products and processes
(f) To develop suitable substitutes for existing materials, products, processes and services
(g) To develop new materials, products, processes and services
(h) To improve manufacturing techniques and processes
(i) To utilise by-products otherwise wasted
(j) To amass technical information leading to a better understanding of material, process or product

Table 1.1. SPECTRUM OF ROME AIR DEVELOPMENT CENTRE*

In-house (creative)	1. Original ideas with bench work experimentation 2. Original study with publication as end item 3. Suggested ideas with bench work experimentation 4. Experiments with unique equipments to derive new techniques or general knowledge 5. Engineering activities to adapt state of art technique to hardware
In-house (non-creative)	6. Technical activity in support of scientific committees, symposia, ad hoc groups 7. State of art experiments 8. Investigations utilising Government facilities against operational equipments 9. Formulation of technical programmes 10. Analyses and consultations required for operational developments (not identifiable with any contract) 11. Test design and evaluation of equipment 12. Design development prior to contracting
Contract support (basic research through systems development)	13. Evaluation of unsolicited proposals 14. Preparation of work statements 15. Engineering support to procurement during negotiations 16. Contract monitoring 17. Acceptance tests exclusive of 11, above

*Adapted from: 'Evaluation of a government-sponsored research and development program', BURGESS, J. S., *IEEE Trans. Engng. Mgmt.*, **EM-13**, No. 2 (1966). Copyright 1966—The Institute of Electrical and Electronic Engineering Inc. Used by permission.

(k) To contribute to the common store of technical knowledge, with the ultimate motive of increased markets through better standards of living.

Similar terms of reference are also relevant to Government work, as shown by the typical spectrum of work in Table 1.1.

PLANNING R & D

It has been said that planning is the tactical means by which the strategy, that is policy, is achieved. It has been stated more precisely[6] as being 'the continuous process for making present risk-taking decisions systematically and with the best possible knowledge of their futurity, organising systematically the effort needed to carry out these decisions and measuring the results of these decisions against the expectations through organised, systematic feedback'.

Forecasts must be associated with probabilities, but through innovation these probabilities can be changed. This can only be done by making decisions in the present. It is the time span between the decision and its result that differentiates *short* and *long range planning*, although these terms are often applied to the period during which expenditure is incurred.

The terms short range and long range are only relative, but an examination of the list of objectives for industrial R & D, given in the previous section, indicates that short range planning can be associated with projects aimed at increasing the profitability of current products or operating procedures. In contrast, long range planning must be concerned with the development of new materials, products and processes, which will affect the growth and character of the organisation.

Relative time spans can differ widely, but are often dictated by the economic life of existing equipment; for example, equipment for the Services is usually considered to have a five year life, whilst for telephone exchanges and power stations, the capital investment dictates about a forty year life. In the first case, short term may mean three years and long term five years, but in the second case the time spans will be longer.

As it is the growth of profits that will supply and/or attract the capital for future expansion, priority is generally given to short term plans. This does not necessarily mean, however, that the function of R & D should be limited to servicing production and sales, although the experience arising from the solution of such problems is often the basis for long term proposals.

The growth of an organisation will depend on the success of its long range planning, but before the plan can be put into operation, two prerequisites must be recognised:

(a) The availability of the necessary capital
(b) The availability of R & D teams with the necessary intellectual and creative competence.

In general, the greater the degree of innovation, the greater will be the potential profits; but at the same time, the risk will be larger. It often follows that the greater the risk, for example in attempting a breakthrough, the greater will be the expenditure involved, with an adverse effect on present profits. In consequence, provided the strategy is justifiable, long range planning must be treated in the same manner as an investment, with the capital assured to carry it to completion.

Because of this financial responsibility, long range planning must pursue goals necessary to the needs of the company, and not just be research for the sake of research. Considering the sum total of R & D work being carried out, the probability is that strategies and tactical programmes will evolve from work done outside the organisation. This does not necessarily mean that there should be no exploratory research, but such work must be directed towards:

(a) New and/or improved strategies
(b) New and/or improved tactics in fulfilment of plans made
(c) Obtaining the knowledge necessary to achieve well selected goals.

Innovation arises from ideas, and in R & D these originate largely from the research staff. In order to give R & D staff the necessary encouragement and freedom of action, detailed planning must be their prerogative; a competent staff is necessary not only to carry out the plan, but also to originate it. This competence must extend to middle management, who will be responsible for selecting and integrating such plans into a proposed programme for submission to top management.

At this stage middle management, to be effective, will be acting in the capacity of staff officers, in that they will endeavour to carry out the detailed effort needed to ensure that the programme adheres to the policy, and that all possible steps have been taken to co-ordinate with the requirements of other sections of the organisation, e.g. finance, production, marketing. It does not mean assuming full responsibility and authority, which are the functions of top management.

This staff requisite also has a feedback to the strategy, in that it must encourage specialisation in various areas. For example, it may provide a basis for division into product groups.

THE RELATIONSHIP OF R & D WITH OTHER FUNCTIONS

It has been demonstrated by comparative studies[7] that R & D associated with *manufacture* is the most effective. It is also generally agreed that most of the research that pays off well and quickly is that which can be identified with specific products, processes or applications. This can only be achieved if there is a similar relationship between R & D and the functions of production, marketing and finance, as must already exist between these functions. As the purpose of the relationship is to achieve mutual understanding, there must be more than liaison between the sections. *Interfaces* between the various functions must be recognised and penetrated. Thus R & D cannot exist in an ivory tower, but must appreciate the functions and learn the language of its colleagues, who should reciprocate.

The presence of an interface relationship does not imply that R & D will carry out the functions of its colleagues, but only that there is a bridge. It is not expected that R & D will carry out marketing, any more than it will become responsible for production, but there must be understanding of all the steps that occur between the formation of an idea, and the marketing of a successful product. The most difficult interface is probably that which exists between R & D and finance, particularly if R & D is not concerned, or has little weight, in the formulation of policy. To carry out its functions, R & D must spend money, whilst the function of finance is to save where possible. This difficulty can only be resolved if the R & D group know enough of the language of finance to be able to correlate their financial needs with future benefits, with the co-operation and understanding of the finance group.

It should be noted that although, as with any other business, financial records of R & D must be kept, this does not in itself imply the existence of an interface. An understanding of how these records are kept, and their implications, are necessary because they are part of the language.

THE ADMINISTRATION TASK

The administration task is to ensure that the R & D group gives maximum assistance in the execution of declared policies by the effective utilisation of scientific knowledge and resources. In consequence there must be organisation, that is, the place of each research worker must be determined, the necessary facilities provided, and all work co-ordinated and controlled. The manner in which this task is carried out must take into account the special problems arising from the nature of R & D:

(a) Low predictability of outcomes
(b) Need to give the worker freedom of judgement and action
(c) Need to foster creativity.

The following chapters attempt to describe the practices used in the various areas of R & D administration. It must be borne in mind, however, that their purpose is to facilitate the operation of the organisation; they must not be allowed to become parasitical, or be considered inviolable.

REFERENCES

1. *Income Tax Act*, Section 340 (1952)
2. *Reviews of Data on Research and Development*, National Science Foundation, Bulletin 26, p. 61, February (1961)
3. SANDERS, G. S., 'Training of management in research', *Res. Mgmt.*, **9**, No. 6, p. 365 (1966)

4. HAGGERTY, P. E., 'Strategies, tactics and research', *Res. Mgmt.*, **9**, No. 3, p. 141 (1966)
5. NISSAN, A. H., 'Similarities and differences between industrial and academic research', *Res. Mgmt.*, **9**, No. 4, p. 211 (1966)
6. DRUCKER, P. F., 'Long range planning means risk taking', Chapter 2, *Long Range Planning for Management*, Ed. Ewing, D. W., Harper and Row (1964)
7. BRECH, F. F. L., 'Organisation for effective R & D', *Management of Research and Development*, British Institute of Management (1964)

BIBLIOGRAPHY

ELBOURNE, E. T., *Fundamentals of Industrial Administration*, **1** and **2**, Macdonald and Evans (1934), (1942)
Report of the Committee on the Management and Control of Research and Development, H.M.S.O. (1961)
KARGER, D. W., MURDICK, R. G., *Managing Engineering and Research*, The Industrial Press, NY (1963)
MORANIAN, T., *The Research and Development Engineer as Manager*, Rutgers, The State University, Holt, Rinehart and Winston (1963)
STOKES, C. A., 'Strengthening the research—marketing—finance team', *Res. Mgmt.*, **9**, No. 6, p. 339 (1966)

Chapter 2

The Research Organisation

One of the most important functions of R & D administration is to allocate responsibility, as from this will be established the delegation of work. Because of the fresh problems and unforeseen requirements that arise constantly in R & D, and because of the need to encourage innovation, authority must stem from knowledge and there must be freedom of action. An organisation that permits this may be described as *'organismic*, as opposed to *mechanistic*, that is, a rigid *line and staff* hierachy which is appropriate when conditions are stable.

Integral with the research organisation must be *supporting staff*, and *services*; provision must also be made for various *peripheral duties* that may be allotted, because of their technical nature.

THE PRINCIPLES OF ORGANISATION

The *principles of organisation* have been stated by L. Urwick as being:

(a) *Functionalisation*—the necessary units of activity involved in the object of the enterprise should be analysed, sub-divided, and arranged in logical groups in such a way as to secure by specialisation the greatest results from individual and combined effort.

(b) *Correspondence*—authority and responsibility must be coterminous, coequal and defined.

(c) *Initiative*—the form of the organisation should be such as to secure from each individual the maximum initiative of which he is capable.

(d) *Co-ordination*—the specialised conduct of activities necessitates arrangements for the systematic interrelating of these activities so as to secure economy of operation. Reference from one activity to another should always take the shortest possible line.

(e) *Continuity*—the structure of the organisation should be such as to provide not only for the activities immediately necessary to secure the object of the enterprise, but also for the continuation of such activities for the full period of operation contemplated in the establishment of the enterprise. This involves a continuous supply of the necessary personnel and arrangements for the systematic improvement of every aspect of operation.

THE ORGANISMIC ORGANISATION

Organisational structures are commonly grouped into four basic types, shown in Fig. 2.1. They are:

(a) *Discipline*, i.e. subject
(b) *Product* or process
(c) *Project*, i.e. problem
(d) *Stage* or *phase* of work.

A *functional* structure is sometimes mentioned in the literature but depending on the context of the word 'function' it can be equated with one of the above structures.

In R & D, the unit of activity in the enterprise is the project, defined as 'all the work related to the research and development of a new product or process.' (This definition is the basis for the control of R & D as shown in Chapter 8.) The project can be multi-disciplined and go through a number of phases, but the pattern of work remains invariable. This pattern may be compared to the growth of an organism, going through the following cycle:

(a) Innovation—the introduction of a new idea
(b) Organisation—the adjustment of the functional relationships
(c) Stabilisation—the precursor to innovation.

Because of the lack of predictability in R & D work, the adjustment of the functional relationships, which in this context can include disciplines and/or phases, must be a continuous process; but there is, as yet, no perfect way of achieving this.

A group that exists solely for the purpose of working on a particular project, as for example a research team in a university, may be called a *pure project structure*. In industry, unless a project is very large, this structure is not favoured, mainly because it gives a low staff utilisation. A method of overcoming this is the *matrix structure* shown in Fig. 2.1(c) which can operate in one of two ways:

(a) Staff are seconded from the discipline to the project when they become both administratively and technically responsible to the *project manager*.* The disciplines carry out relevant central research functions such as fundamental research and special investigations, to which staff return on cessation of the project

---

*The titles associated with the responsibilities are used throughout this book for the sake of clarity, but in particular organisations both the titles and the allocation of duties may differ.

11

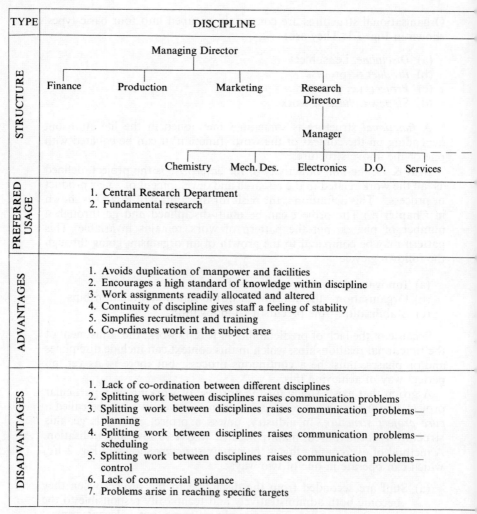

TYPE	DISCIPLINE				
STRUCTURE	Managing Director Finance Production Marketing Research Director Manager Chemistry Mech. Des. Electronics D.O. Services				
PREFERRED USAGE	1. Central Research Department 2. Fundamental research				
ADVANTAGES	1. Avoids duplication of manpower and facilities 2. Encourages a high standard of knowledge within discipline 3. Work assignments readily allocated and altered 4. Continuity of discipline gives staff a feeling of stability 5. Simplifies recruitment and training 6. Co-ordinates work in the subject area				
DISADVANTAGES	1. Lack of co-ordination between different disciplines 2. Splitting work between disciplines raises communication problems 3. Splitting work between disciplines raises communication problems—planning 4. Splitting work between disciplines raises communication problems—scheduling 5. Splitting work between disciplines raises communication problems—control 6. Lack of commercial guidance 7. Problems arise in reaching specific targets				

(a)

Fig. 2.1. (a), (b), (c), (d).

TYPE	PRODUCT/PROCESS
STRUCTURE	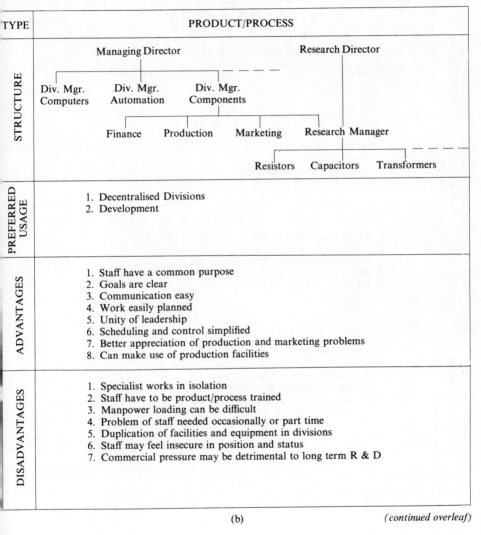
PREFERRED USAGE	1. Decentralised Divisions 2. Development
ADVANTAGES	1. Staff have a common purpose 2. Goals are clear 3. Communication easy 4. Work easily planned 5. Unity of leadership 6. Scheduling and control simplified 7. Better appreciation of production and marketing problems 8. Can make use of production facilities
DISADVANTAGES	1. Specialist works in isolation 2. Staff have to be product/process trained 3. Manpower loading can be difficult 4. Problem of staff needed occasionally or part time 5. Duplication of facilities and equipment in divisions 6. Staff may feel insecure in position and status 7. Commercial pressure may be detrimental to long term R & D

(b)

(continued overleaf)

Basic R & D structures

TYPE	PROJECT CUM DISCIPLINE (MATRIX)
STRUCTURE	R & D MANAGER DISCIPLINE A B C D PROJECT 1 ,, 2 ,, 3
PREFERRED USAGE	1. Multi-disciplines 2. Basic through to development
ADVANTAGES	1. Target objectives are clear 2. Facilitates good co-ordination and teamwork 3. Work is most likely to proceed to schedule 4. Interaction of disciplines on common problem can assist 5. Job situation is not static
DISADVANTAGES	As product structure 1. No year to year continuity for staff 2. Manpower loading can be difficult 3. It creates an artificial discipline

(c)

Fig. 2.1. (continued)

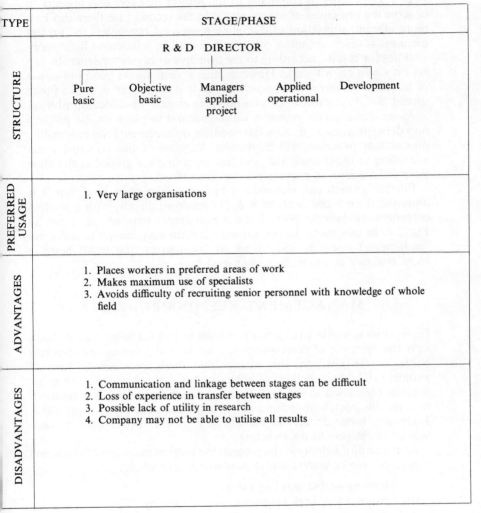

TYPE	STAGE/PHASE				
STRUCTURE	R & D DIRECTOR				
	Pure basic	Objective basic	Managers applied project	Applied operational	Development
PREFERRED USAGE	1. Very large organisations				
ADVANTAGES	1. Places workers in preferred areas of work 2. Makes maximum use of specialists 3. Avoids difficulty of recruiting senior personnel with knowledge of whole field				
DISADVANTAGES	1. Communication and linkage between stages can be difficult 2. Loss of experience in transfer between stages 3. Possible lack of utility in research 4. Company may not be able to utilise all results				

(d)

(b) The *discipline manager* retains administrative control of his staff, who are only responsible to the project manager on technical issues.

The first alternative would appear to be the best management practice, since it gives unity of command to the project manager and appears to observe the principles of organisation. In the second case there can be a more efficient utilisation of discipline resources; but unless the project manager is given authority over the line staff in relation to his responsibilities for results, according to the principle of correspondence, he can act only as a co-ordinator. However, this system allows good utilisation of technical resources and knowledge, provided the staff is not so thinly spread that it is unable to concentrate long enough on difficult problems.

As an organisation grows, it will be natural to place similar projects into departments and thus an intermediate management level grouped by products or processes will be formed. Variants of this structure arise, according to those disciplines and functions that are graded at the same intermediate level to provide peripheral services.

Further growth can introduce a higher management level, but it is more usual for those facets of R & D concerned directly with a product or process to become part of the departmental structure as shown in Fig. 2.1. In this event the central organisation may remain to carry out fundamental research and to act as consultants, the result being a *stage structure* at top management level.

MANAGEMENT RESPONSIBILITIES

Each position within an organisation must be defined fully, in accordance with the principle of correspondence, to show the duties and responsibilities of the position; this ensures that there are clear cut lines of authority. The best method of achieving this is to draw up a *job specification*, (discussed in the next chapter) which must take into account, for a specific post, both technical knowledge and personal characteristics. There are, however, certain management aspects which must be considered in relation to the structure.

As the unit of activity is the project, the bottom management level will consist of *project leaders* whose responsibilities include:

(a) Planning and scheduling the work
(b) Ensuring the work progresses as planned, by:
    1. Monitoring progress (and costs)
    2. Co-ordinating functions and/or disciplines
    3. Instituting corrective actions as necessary
(c) Reporting status of work to management and making progress reports
(d) Implementing management approved changes, for example:
    1. Changes in goals or specifications
    2. Decision to cut-off

   3. Changes in priorities
   4. Changes in allocation of manpower or resources
 (e) Keeping the estimate under review.

The superior level or levels is commonly termed *middle management*. In R & D, a multi-layered structure is not favoured as it can give rise to communication difficulties. There may, however, be an intermediate level of *project manager*, whose duties will be substantially the same as a project leader, but who will supervise two or more project leaders, or perhaps one comparatively large project. The duties of middle management or the *research manager*, will encompass:

(a) Preparing and submitting for Board approval:
   1. Proposals for new projects
   2. Financial and manpower budgets
   3. Proposals for capital expenditure
(b) Keeping approved proposals under review, and advising the Board of changes
(c) Allocating manpower and resources, including:
   1. Priorities
   2. Recruitment of staff
(d) Ensuring work progresses as planned by:
   1. Reviewing status with project leader
   2. Giving assistance as necessary
   3. Not permitting unauthorised work
(e) Approving changes to the plan of work, e.g.
   1. Goals or specifications
   2. Cut-off decision
(f) Maintaining interface relationships with:
   1. Customers
   2. Finance, marketing, production
(g) Providing the impetus to the organisation, by:
   1. Fostering innovation
   2. Advising top management on organisational changes.

Where the research department is of significant size or importance, the top management position may be held by a *Research Director* in the United Kingdom, or a *Vice President* (Research) in the United States. In such a position he will have two functions, the first arising from his legal position as an *officer of the company*, the second as an *executive*.

In the United Kingdom, the *Companies Act* of 1967 lays down the general responsibilities of directors as these relate to their appointment and discharge, and their duties to shareholders and finance. The Act is only specific with regard to the functions of the Managing Director and Secretary, the functions of other directors being limited to sharing in the ultimate responsibility for the direction of policy in all aspects that can affect the company. Thus, although a director may have a special executive function such as research, and advises his colleagues during the exercise of that function, he is equally responsible with them in reaching

17

policy decisions. Such decisions must be made taking into account the advice given by other functions, such as finance and marketing, which may affect or complicate the issue which is ultimately, the justification of all financial expenditure.

The executive functions of a research director have been described[1] as:

(a) Defining the general objectives of a company's research programme

(b) Executive management of the research programme, i.e. its organisation and administration, although various aspects may be delegated to the research manager.

(c) Control of non-research ancillary functions within the research department, e.g. finance, recruitment, training

(d) Advising the Board in his technical capacity by:

   1. Translating and justifying the technical objectives of the various projects which have been generated by staff within and outside his department, and are accepted and supported by him.

   2. Demonstrating to what extent the research programme, in whole or in detail, implements Board policy not only in objectives but in the individual importance attaching to each project

   3. Determining how far projects meet the requirements of departments outside his control (designers, production engineers, etc.)

(e) Acquainting the research department, through his own knowledge of Board discussions, or otherwise, of the demands, requests, fears, unresolved worries, and 'hunches' of those who require technical assistance.

THE COMMUNICATION PROBLEM

It has been suggested[2] that *communication* has three aspects:

(a) To inform, which refers to what an individual does

(b) To instruct, that is how he does it

(c) To motivate, showing why he does it.

The effect of each aspect may be influenced by the other aspects, so that the properties of the communication will depend on the communication itself, and may be modified by the receiver.

The input and output of an R & D organisation may be considered to be *information*, processed by means of *instructions* because of *motivations* given. The initial information will be the objectives, perhaps given in the form of a *statement of requirements*, or *specification*. During the life of the project there will be information:

(a) Originating outside the organisation, e.g. from published matter

(b) Arising internally, for example:

   1. Results of experiments

   2. Availability of resources.

The extent and relevance or validity of the information will be judged by the receiver, with an effect on his purposeful state. The result may be that he will give or seek instructions, that is, he will communicate. Hence all significant matters must be recorded and this implies standardisation in drafting and transmission. The need for this is twofold: first, because of research workers' antipathy towards paperwork; secondly because an individual's judgement is involved in assessing what is significant.

Instructions will originate from communications in one or more of the three aspects. In an R & D project, the principle instructions arise from information, and a mark of efficiency must be the time span elapsing between when the information originated and when the instructions were carried out. Furthermore, as the properties of a message depend not only on the message but also on the receiver, it is important that instructions are precise and that resulting actions are monitored; that is, there is feedback of information.

The motivation aspect of communication must always be borne in mind, since it will affect productivity and creativity.

Communication may be summarised as: the best method of ensuring that all significant information is properly recorded and transmitted to the decision making authority, who will then issue precise instructions, the whole process taking the minimum feasible time. Bad communications can nullify good administrative practices, as they will result in loss of control through:

(a) Reduced effectiveness of planning
(b) Retardation of related work
(c) Lack of co-ordination.

The traditional method of ensuring fast communication is to have clear cut lines of authority which are not extended. With extended lines (which arise in a multi-layered structure) or when communication must be made horizontally across a structure, the problem is more complex, and it is only since the advent of *network techniques* such as PERT (see Chapter 7) that a feasible solution has arisen. With the extension of such techniques to multi-projects, the function cum discipline orientated structure appears favoured, even for a large organisation.

THE RESEARCH ENVIRONMENT

Within a research organisation, an environment must be fostered that will enable the average man to give of his best, it being appreciated that only the outstanding scientists are truly creative.

The need for establishing a formal structure has been discussed; but overlapping this must be an informal organisation which exists to meet the needs of individuals and the groups which they form. This must be recognised, since it creates the independent and unstifled atmosphere that fosters creativity.

The needs of research workers have been stated as: 'problems of own origin, with adequate facilities, in a pleasant place with colleagues of similar tastes, in a society that values this kind of work and is willing to pay a competitive price for it'. This, however, is idealistic, particularly as people differ in their attitudes to various aspects of work, such as time-keeping and paperwork. In practice the aim must be to prevent frustration and active dissatisfaction.

The objectives of a scientist must include his personal competence. This can only be engendered by:

(a) Recognising the individuality of each person's contribution
(b) Being concerned in other's ideas and feelings, without necessarily affirming (because he is a superior), or being antagonistic (to a junior)
(c) Showing trust in individuals, their ideas, and feelings.

These qualities can be encouraged in a group by *subordinate-centred leadership*,[3] which is illustrated in Fig. 2.2. At the extreme limit there is what is termed *participative management*, each individual having equal powers and authority. Although this method has its protagonists,[4] surveys seem to show that something more to the left on the scale gives the best job satisfaction, and confidence in management. Such management, however, is only practical if a group is small, and this can mean decentralisation of the organisation.

An environmental factor to which due consideration is not always given, is the *support ratio*. This is defined by the National Science Foundation as 'the number of non-professional assistants supporting each professional scientist or engineer'. Such support may be categorised as *technical* or *administrative*.

Technical support should be aimed at cutting down routine duties for the professional staff, thereby assisting in their optimum utilisation. Such support may cover the provision of a drawing office and model shop, as well as laboratory assistants. The extent of the support must depend on the type and nature of the work, for example, a test laboratory would be expected to have more support workers than a pure research laboratory.[5]

The main purpose of administration is to facilitate the operation of the organisation so that objectives are obtained effectively and expeditiously.[6] These practices should not absorb the energies of the scientists, otherwise frustration and poor morale will result. Administrative support must, therefore be provided and this can be organised conveniently in a *project control office*. The provision of such support has the added advantage that the cost of the administrative practices can be determined, and this may prevent their proliferation.

The average support ratio in both British and American research laboratories is approximately unity overall, and about one-third for direct support. For any individual laboratory the best guidance to the adequacy of the support ratio will be the absence of complaints from the staff.

Finally, *unassigned time* should be allocated to each research worker to enable him to follow up points of interest that may not be directly relevant to the project. This includes, for example, attending conferences or reading technical publications, and is important since such matters

20

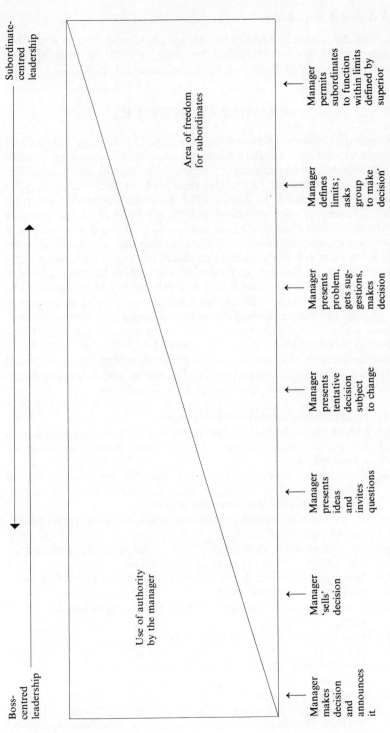

Fig. 2.2. Continuum of leadership behaviour. From 'How to choose a leadership pattern', TANNENBAUM, R. and SCHMIDT, W. H., Harv. Busin. Rev., 36, March-April 1958. Reproduced by courtesy of the authors and Harvard Business Review

are often the source of ideas. The average unassigned time in a number of laboratories has been found to be about 10% of the total working hours, and is charged as an overhead (see Table 6.3, p. 82).

PERIPHERAL SERVICES

Research departments often embrace a number of ancillary services and accumulate certain secondary functions. Ancillary services arise when the department is large enough to become independent, and will include such matters as finance, contracts, personnel, each of which may be functionally responsible to a head office. Secondary functions are those which, because of their technical nature, are allotted to the research department. More than thirty such activities, including design, technical sales, training, library services, technical publications, are classified under the generic term *non-research* in Appendix X of *Proposed Standard Practice for Surveys of Research and Development*[7]. These functions can play an important part in the growth of a research group and its parent company, for example in the training and supply of specialist staff, preparing the ground for future developments by the supply of technical information, and enhancing the public image of the organisation by publications and other evidence of scientific ability.[1] In industrial research, the function of design may include not only development, but also certain peripheral services; the definition[8] of the job of an electronics design department, for example, includes the following duties:

(a) To help formulate future sales policy
(b) To help turn sales ideas for the future into operational requirements
(c) To write target technical specifications based on customer requirements
(d) To undertake investigation work to establish the practicability of incorporating new techniques into equipments being developed. To write appropriate notes and reports
(e) To develop equipments to meet the target technical specifications:
　　1. At the right time
　　2. At a reasonable development cost (related to the prospect of cost recovery in the marketing programme)
　　3. In a way which can be manufactured in the production department at an economic price
(f) To make, or assist in, field trials of new equipments. To report results
(g) To supply information to production:
　　1. Drawings
　　2. Test specifications and test certificates
　　3. Suggested production test gear requirements
(h) To supply information to sales:
　　1. The technical specification (based on the target technical specification, but correcting it in the light of development experience)

22

2. The draft technical handbook
3. The draft operating handbook
4. Field test gear schedule
5. Suggest ancillary items and spares schedules

(i) To be the department of technical appeal for all other departments
   —particularly to the inspection, test and field service departments
(j) To keep management informed of technical progress.

REFERENCES

1. FINNISTON, H. M., 'The research program and company policy', *Res. Mgmt.*, **9**, No. 4 p. 229 (1966)
2. MARTIN, M. W., 'The management of value of scientific information', *Operations Research in Research and Development*, Ed. Dean, B. W., John Wiley, NY (1963)
3. TANNENBAUM, R., SCHMIDT, W. H., 'How to choose a leadership pattern', *Harv. Busin. Rev.*, **36**, No. 2, p. 95 (1958)
4. GMITTER, G. T., 'The industrial R & D scientist and his environment', *Res. Mgmt.*, **9**, No. 2, p. 115 (1966)
5. ANDREA, R. E., *The Ratio of Support to Professional Manpower in R & D Laboratories*, Research Thesis, University of Chicago, ASTIA report AD 287809 (1962)
6. SUBNAMANIAN, S. K., 'Organising industrial research in India', *Res. Mgmt.*, **9**, No. 6 p. 351 (1966)
7. *Proposed Standard Practice for Surveys of Research and Development*, OECD Publication DAS/PD/62.47, 3rd revision
8. HARRIS, K. E., 'The task of the industrial development engineer—and the management of design', *Syst. Commun.*, **2**, p. 15, April (1966)

BIBLIOGRAPHY

BUSH, G. P., HATTERY, L. H., (Eds.), *Scientific Research, its Administration and Organisation*, American University Press (1950)
ANTHONY, R. N., *Management Controls in Industrial Research Organisations*, Harvard University, Boston (1952)
The Direction of Research Establishments, Symposium, National Physical Laboratory, 1956, H.M.S.O. (1957)
MACGREGOR, D., *The Human Side of Enterprise*, McGraw-Hill Inc. NY (1960)
BURNS, T., STALKER, C. M., *The Management of Innovation*, Tavistock Publications (1961)
Optimum Use of Engineering Talent, American Management Association Report 58, NY (1961)
Adaptations of Scientists in an Independent Research Organisation, a Case Study, prepared by Stanford Research Institute, California, for Behavioural Sciences Division, Air Force Office of Scientific Research Defence Documentation Centre AD 407182 (1963)
KARGER, D. W., MURDICK, R. G., *Managing Engineering and Research*, The Industrial Press, NY, (1963)
MORANIAN, T., *The Research and Development Engineer as Manager*, Rutgers, The State University, Holt, Rinehart and Winston (1963)
BLAIN, I., *Structure in Management: A Study of Different Forms and their Effectiveness*, National Institute of Industrial Psychology (1964)
BRECH, F. F. L. *et al.*, *Management of Research and Development*, British Institute of Management (1964)
GLATT, E., 'Research and application: an approval to management problems in an R & D laboratory', *IEEE Trans. Engng. Mgmt.*, **EM-11**, No. 3 p. 90 (1964)
LAZAR, R. G., KELLNER, A. D., 'Personnel and organisation development in an R & D matrix—overlay operation', *IEEE Trans. Engng. Mgmt.*, **EM-11**, No. 2, p. 78 (1964)

R & D Administration

ORTH, C. D., *et al.*, *Administering Research and Development*, The Dorsey Press, (1964)

PELZ, D. C., 'The creative years and the research environment', *IEEE Trans. Engng. Mgmt.*, **EM-11**, No. 1, p. 23 (1964)

COCKROFT, SIR J. (Ed.), *The Organisation of Research Establishments*, Cambridge University Press (1965)

DUCKWORTH, J. C., 'Incentives to innovation and invention', *Electron. & Power*, **11**, p. 186, June (1965)

PEARCE, J. G., 'Research organisation for adequate creative freedom', *Bull. Inst. Phys.*, **16**, No. 11, p. 439 (1965)

SEILER, R. E., *Improving the Effectiveness of Research and Development*, McGraw-Hill Inc., NY (1965)

STANLEY, A. O., WHITE, K. K., *Organising the R & D Function*, American Management Association Inc. (1965)

ARGYRIS, C., 'Interpersonal competence, organisational milieu, and innovation', *Res. Mgmt.*, **9**, No. 2, p. 71 (1966)

HUNTER, J. H., 'Communications in an R & D organisation', *Res. & Development*, **17** p. 26, July (1966)

WALLMARK, J. T., SELLERBERG, B., 'Efficiency vs size of research teams', *IEEE Trans. Engng., Mgmt.*, **EM-13**, No. 3, p. 137 (1966)

Proc. Ann. Conf. Ind. Res., Columbia University, USA

Chapter 3

Staff—Placement and Training

It is axiomatic that an organisation is only as effective as the staff comprising it. Staff cannot be recruited, except at the lowest levels, purely on skill and an attempt then made to fit an organisation around them. This implies, not that the organisation should be immutable, but that each position within it should be defined; on placement of staff, a feedback process should then permit the structure to be optimised. This process must be continuous, since the qualities of the staff will change with experience and training. The R & D manager must ensure that this change is of benefit not only to the individual, but to the organisation as a whole, leading to retention of staff, the accumulation of new knowledge and techniques, and increased efficiency.

JOB SPECIFICATION

The preparation of a *job specification* performs certain functions:

(a) It is an essential part of the *analysis* of the organisation; and only by the preparation of a specification can duties and responsibilities be defined clearly
(b) It defines the requirements of the job; this is necessary to ensure the best placement of available staff
(c) If the position cannot be filled from within the company, the precise definition of the job helps in obtaining Board approval for recruitment; this is part of the budgetary process, described in Chapter 4
(d) It enables the personnel department to decide the specific aims of a recruitment programme and to sort out applicants for interview.

Accepting that the details of an organisation must depend primarily on the plan of work, the starting point of a job specification must be an area of work to be accomplished within the plan. It is conducive to clear thinking if this area is sub-divided into administration, discipline and function. From this the responsibilities and duties can be defined

25

Table 3.1. THE JOB SPECIFICATION OF A MAJOR U.K. COMPANY

XYZ COMPANY R & D Division
JOB SPECIFICATION
POST

DEPARTMENT:	Test
PROJECT:	Aircraft Project/Activity No.
DISCIPLINE:	Electrical Engineering
FUNCTION:	Systems testing of high temperature components
TITLE:	Senior Development Engr. GRADE:

RESPONSIBLE TO
1. Function — Manager, Test Department
2. Line — Project Leaders—Aircraft Systems

DUTIES — Group Leader

RESPONSIBILITIES
1. Technical — Design of test rigs
Investigations and analysis of designs
Initiates design improvement modifications
2. Administrative — Plans and assigns work of staff (2 Engrs.)
(3 Asst. Engrs.)
Checks work of staff
3. Financial — Wrong decisions may cause damage to expensive components and equipment
4. Other Departments — Instructs Production Test and checks their methods
5. Customer — Contact with customers and their development engineers

QUALIFICATIONS
1. Academic Standard — B.Sc. (Eng.)
2. Training — Apprenticeship
3. Experience — 6 years as development engineer
4. Specialisation — Environmental testing

PERSONAL QUALITIES
1. Initiative — Must be capable of solving difficult problems and making decisions
2. Creativity — Not absolutely necessary
3. Dependability — High degree of accuracy and care required
4. Co-operative — Inter-departmental relationships
5. Leadership — Staff of 5
6. Expression — (a) Oral—reasonable
(b) Writing—report writing should be good

WORKING CONDITIONS
1. Environment — Laboratory
2. Mental strain — Considerable
3. Physical strain — Slight

NOTES TO PERSONNEL DEPT.
1. To be filled by* — (a) Internal transfer (b) Recruitment:
(*delete as applicable)   Replacement/
Authorised staff increase
2. Date by which post should be filled
3. Period of in-job training envisaged — 1 year
4. Salary Grade: — C
5. Anticipated life of post — 5 years
6. Future prospects — Function manager retires in 3 years

and the qualities necessary to perform them satisfactorily, derived. An example of a job specification from the records of a major United Kingdom company is shown in Table 3.1.

It should be a matter of policy that intermediate and higher grade posts are filled whenever possible by internal promotion. The implementation of this policy is discussed later in this Chapter.

Since all jobs are dependent on the plan of work, staff must be allocated as and when required; the mechanics of this process are described in Chapter 7. To ensure that the plan is adhered to, each job specification must stipulate the date by which the position should be filled. Such dates also enable the recruiter to formulate his plan of action. Again, as the job of work must have a finite life, long range staffing requirements (and associated long range budget) may have to be stated in order to justify recruitment, and to give the prospective employee a realistic forecast of his prospects.

ACADEMIC QUALIFICATIONS

Since science and engineering are 'open' professions (unlike medicine and law), qualified and unqualified persons may work side by side and do work of equal significance. The main purpose of a qualification, therefore, is to indicate not only the extent of formal training, but also the mental capabilities of a person and the degree of application to work of which he is capable. An unqualified or partially qualified person, however, may be able to demonstrate these qualities by records of achievements such as published articles, or patents.

Table 3.2 attempts to indicate the relative status of qualifications in the United Kingdom and the United States. It does not necessarily mean that qualifications on the same level are equivalent, since syllabuses can differ.

In the United Kingdom, the *scientific assistant* or *junior technician* grade usually calls for possession of the Ordinary National Certificate or Diploma. Such courses are designed to be broad in concept, to give a suitable basis for further education; they normally last for four years but students with G.C.E. 'O' levels may start at the third year (O' level). A diploma which is academically equivalent is the Full Technological Certificate of the City and Guilds of London Institute, (in conjunction with the Institute of Science Technology since 1959). Being more specialised, however, this may reach a higher standard in a particular aspect. The grades of the Institute of Medical Laboratory Technicians are broadly similar. These qualifications appear to relate to two years' study in the United States in subjects relevant to the profession, and for which an Associate Degree is sometimes awarded.

For a *senior scientific assistant*, or technician capable of working on his own, the Higher National Certificate or Diploma, or City and Guilds Advanced Certificate indicates a high standard. Such qualifications are obtained by attending evening or day release classes, and may be associated with an apprenticeship or other practical training. The

27

Table 3.2. TECHNICAL AND PROFESSIONAL QUALIFICATIONS IN THE UNITED KINGDOM AND THE UNITED STATES

United States of America		United Kingdom			
University	Professional Institute	University	Technological University	Polytechnic	Professional Institutes
University entrance (Freshman Year)		G.C.E. Ordinary (O) levels	G.C.E. Ordinary (O) levels	G.C.E. Ordinary (O) levels	Preliminary *
Associate Degree		University entrance G.C.E. Advanced (A) levels	University entrance G.C.E. Advanced (A) levels O.N.C./O.N.D. with credits	G.C.E. Advanced (A) levels O.N.C./O.N.D. with credits Higher National Certificate (H.N.C.)	Part I*
				Higher National Diploma (H.N.D.)	
B.S.*	Member*	B.Sc.* Ordinary (Sometimes called 'Pass')			
		B.Sc.* Honours† (with 1st, 2nd or 3rd class, latter sometimes called 'Pass')	B.Tech or B.Sc. Honours (with 1st, 2nd or 3rd class)	B.Sc.* Honours† (with 1st, 2nd or 3rd class)	Graduate*
M.S. (status depends on that of B.S.)	Senior Member*	Postgraduate Diploma M.Sc. or M.Phil.	Postgraduate Diploma M.Tech or M.Sc.	M.Sc.*	Member†
Ph.D.	Fellow*	Ph.D.	Ph.D.	Ph.D.*	Fellow†
		D.Sc.	D.Tech or D.Sc.		
*Status of B.S. will depend both on college and number of semester hours shown on transcript for major subjects—27 may be considered equivalent to U.K. B.Sc. Ordinary	*Grades are indicative of professional standing and not of academic qualifications	*At Cambridge or Oxford the degree of B.A. or M.A. is awarded †London University equivalent is B.Sc. (Special) or B.Sc. (Eng.)		*Awarded by the Council for National Academic Awards (C.N.A.A.) †The first degree was formerly Dip.Tech.	*Partial or full exemption can be given by other examinations †Election to these Grades depends on professional standing

American equivalent would appear to be a B.S. with at least fifteen semester hours in the major subject, obtained under similar conditions.

In the United Kingdom, the Civil Service and some industrial laboratories have a grade termed *Experimental Officer*. The qualifications for this are normally a B.Sc. Ordinary Degree, Higher National Certificate with Endorsements, or Higher National Diploma, although experience may be considered in lieu. Experimental officers are considered to be professional staff, capable of working on their own initiative, although under the general supervision of more senior staff. They are normally considered for work of a routine character, for example chemical analysis and the detail work of development and design. In many cases such staff prove themselves the equal of those with higher qualifications. The American equivalent appears to be a B.S. with about twenty-seven semester hours spent on the major subject, the grading being that of a *senior technician*.

There is relative uniformity in the United Kingdom with regard to degree requirements, both in curricula and standards. In the United States, however, examination standards vary with the number of semester hours booked; this in turn depends on the number of subjects studied. When a course at a particular college is accredited either by a professional organisation such as the Engineers Council for Professional Development or by a major regional association, the standard is usually equal to that of a first degree in the United Kingdom.[1] A difficulty often arises, however, in determining which courses are accredited at which colleges; it is then necessary to ascertain the number of semester hours shown on the transcript, together with information as to the scholastic status of the college.

The award of an approved degree gives exemption from the graduate-ship examination of the senior professional associations in the United Kingdom. *Corporate* membership, however, is only awarded after several years have been spent in an approved responsible position; the number of years can depend on the class of degree. Associations in the United States do not have examinations, membership being awarded on the basis of experience and standing as reported by proposers. Table 3.3 lists the scientific and engineering professional institutes in the United Kingdom.

A graduate in the United Kingdom can proceed to:

(a) *Postgraduate diploma*—this is obtained by examination after attending a one year full time course in one subject. It is becoming rare, as such courses now usually lead to a Masters degree
(b) *M.Sc.*—this may be gained by (a) advanced study and examination, with usually a dissertation (i.e. not necessarily original work); or (b) research and a thesis. Some universities now differentiate the latter by the new degree of M.Phil.
(c) *Ph.D.*—direct entry is normally limited to honours graduates. The course is usually of three years' duration, consisting of advanced study, a research project and submission of a thesis.

29

Table 3.3. SCIENTIFIC AND ENGINEERING PROFESSIONAL INSTITUTES IN THE UNITED KINGDOM

Institute	Address
*Royal Aeronautical Society	4 Hamilton Place London W.1
Institution of Agricultural Engineers	Rickmansworth, Herts
Institute of Biology	4 Queen's Gate, London S.W.7
Institute of Brewing	33 Clarges Street, London W.1
Institute of Ceramics	Shelton, Stoke-on-Trent, Staffs
Association of Consulting Engineers	2 Victoria Street, London S.W.1
*Institution of Chemical Engineers	16 Belgrave Square, London S.W.1
Royal Institute of Chemistry	30 Russell Square, London W.C.1
*Institution of Civil Engineers	Gt. George Street, Westminster, London S.W.1
*Institution of Electrical Engineers	Savoy Place, Victoria Embankment, London W.C.2
Institution of Electrical and Electronics Technician Engineers	26 Bloomsbury Square, London W.C.1
*Institution of Electronic and Radio Engineers	9 Bedford Square, London W.C.1
Institute of Fuel	18 Devonshire Street, London W.1
*Institution of Gas Engineers	17 Grosvenor Crescent, London S.W.1
Royal Institute of Public Health and Hygiene	28 Portland Place, London W.1
Institution of Heating and Ventilating Engineers	49 Cadogan Square, London S.W.1
Institution of Highway Engineers	47 Victoria Street, London S.W.1
Institution of Locomotive Engineers	28 Victoria Street, London S.W.1
*Institute of Marine Engineers	The Memorial Building, 76 Mark Lane, London E.C.3
*Institution of Mechanical Engineers	1 Birdcage Walk, Westminster, London S.W.1
Institution of Metallurgists	17 Belgrave Square, London S.W.1
*Institution of Mining Engineers (for coal and ironstone mining)	3 Grosvenor Crescent, London S.W.1
*Institution of Mining and Metallurgy	44 Portland Place, London W.1
*Institution of Municipal Engineers	25 Eccleston Square, London S.W.1
*Royal Institution of Naval Architects	10 Upper Belgrave Street, London S.W.1
The Chartered Institute of Patent Agents,	Staple Inn Buildings, London W.C.1
Institute of Physics and the Physical Society	1 Lowther Gardens, Prince Consort Road, London S.W.7
*Institution of Production Engineers	10 Chesterfield Street, London W.1
*Institution of Structural Engineers	11 Upper Belgrave Street, London S.W.1
Institute of Transport	80 Portland Place, London W.1
Institution of Water Engineers	11 Pall Mall, London S.W.1
Institute of Welding	54 Princes Gate, London S.W.7

*Corporate members of these Institutes are CHARTERED ENGINEERS and may use the letters C.Eng.

The standard of work is higher than that called for in the M.Sc.

(d) *D.Sc.*—this is awarded normally only to an applicant who holds a higher degree and who can produce a body of published work which makes a positive contribution to knowledge. This degree is not generally awarded until several years after graduation.

Because of the varying standards of the first degree in the United States, many colleges require students proceeding to an M.S. degree to take an entrance examination. Courses may be designated and a thesis may be required. In general, a minimum of thirty semester hours is required so that standards do not vary as much as for a first degree, even so, the degree can equate from a British B.Sc. Honours to M.Sc. In both the United Kingdom and the United States, Ph.D. degrees appear to be on the same level, although in some cases the American degree may be superior. It should be noted that American colleges may designate their doctorate by different titles, but this does not necessarily imply different standards.[2] Some colleges award a degree which is intermediate between that of M.Sc. and the doctorate.

In the United States there are also professional examinations. These are, in effect, licences to practice a profession on the public. As standards vary widely between different cities and states, no cognisance can be placed on this qualification unless there is a full knowledge of the particular requirements that have been met.

PERSONAL QUALITIES

Personal qualities by their nature cannot be defined as precisely as academic qualifications and training. They are, however, no less important and should be considered carefully in relation to the job and not to the type of man the manager prefers. It is important to specify only those qualities considered necessary for the performance of the work.

To illustrate this, consider *initiative* or, as it is sometimes expressed, *motivation*. An individual having a high degree of this faculty will be ambitious, driving, assume responsibility and take risks in making decisions. Even if he can control these actions, such a person will move to another job unless his position offers him rapid promotion and increase in responsibility.

Allied to initiative may be *creativity*. This attribute is almost impossible to assess, although evidence of its existence is afforded by original work, published papers, patents, etc. This quality is of particular importance in the composition of an R & D organisation, and a highly creative person should not be employed where his freedom is restricted, either by the nature of the work or his superiors.

By *dependability* is meant honesty and reliability; reliability in carrying out a job correctly and properly in accordance with instructions, and honesty in the presentation of results. Once again there are degrees to which these attributes are desirable; a highly dependable person may in fact be a stickler for procedure, whilst someone more erratic may be found who can be relied on to produce results.

In any organisation, co-operation is essential. People can be too co-operative, however, in that they are always ready to assist someone else rather than do their own work. Perhaps the better attribute is the ability to establish good personal relationships.

A great deal has been said and written about the quality of *leadership* and how this can be developed. Obviously when staff is to be controlled, a good leader is better than a bad leader. The assets needed are similar to those required for establishing co-operation. But in addition, there must be an awareness of what the staff desires from him—competence, giving credit for work done whilst taking full responsibility for mistakes, allowing freedom of action whilst being aware of everything occurring. This quality of leadership is perhaps the most elusive, and when found should be utilised to the full. It must be remembered, however, that many positions in an organisation do not call for a high degree of leadership; a senior post such as consultant, for example, may not require any leadership ability.

Expression may be both *oral* or *written*. A person who has to 'sell' the company will obviously require to be quick thinking and ready with his tongue. Here, however, the extreme can be dangerous, since a company's response to such a person may be one of suspicion. For most research work, it is sufficient if a person can express himself adequately verbally, and in writing. If necessary reports and articles may be written by a professional copywriter supplied with the facts.

RECRUITING

The cost of recruiting technical staff is such that a precise recruitment plan is always necessary; the R & D manager must assist the personnel department in the formulation of this plan.

The methods of recruitment can be summarised as follows:[3]

(a) *The use of existing leads and contacts*
  1. Existing staff
  2. Records of past interviews and applications
  3. Personal contacts of the staff
(b) *Employment agencies.* A suitable agency or agencies must be selected carefully and a personal relationship established. Agencies may be found from the American Management Association or the British Institute of Management Directory of Consultants. Advertisements in newspapers can also provide suitable names
(c) *College Placement Offices* or *University Appointments Boards.* These are usually on a more formal basis in the United States than in the United Kingdom. It is important to keep the appropriate staff informed of the work of the organisation

(d) *Advertising*
  1. Professional and technical journals
  2. Newspapers
     This is the most popular method of recruiting for specific vacancies, since it publicises the company and, if suitably displayed, perhaps attracts persons who are not necessarily seeking a new position
(e) *Recruiting trips.* These should be planned carefully, prior arrangements being made for a number of interviews, and the trip perhaps timed to coincide with a conference or exhibition
(f) *Career centres.* In the United States such centres have been established in various cities, each being sponsored by a number of companies who pay a fixed fee. The applicant needs to complete only one resumé to have it reviewed by a large number of firms; he need not travel to an interview
(g) *Internal referral programmes.* This is an extension of (a)2 in which the staff are asked for the names of friends in other firms who would be interested in moving. A reward is often associated with a successful referral. This method is perhaps more applicable to the recruitment of junior staff
(h) *Search firms.* This is an expensive method, so is limited normally to the recruiting of senior staff. A search firm undertakes to find suitable applicants, the potential employer not being disclosed unless the applicant is suitable and interested in the position.

An analysis of the results obtained in the past by the various recruiting methods, together with an analysis of reasons for refusal, should enable an effective recruitment plan to be made.

INTERVIEWING

An interview has two purposes, first to evaluate the man for the job, and secondly to sell the company and the job to the applicant.

To assist in evaluating a person, many companies commence the interview with a psychological test carried out by a specialist in this field. Such tests are not meant to replace the manager's evaluation, but to assist him in verifying his impressions. The tests may cover intelligence, personality, and interest. As there are a number of variants, the manager should acquaint himself with the test used by his organisation, appreciating that the results of such tests are never claimed to be infallible; at the best, they are only indicators.

To evaluate a person, it is essential to get him talking freely and at ease. The starting point is usually the *application form*, questions being directed to determine the extent of the applicant's knowledge, rather than what he does not know. If possible, references should be checked before the interview; this should preferably be done by telephone, since true opinions, particularly regarding weaknesses, are more readily

33

expressed verbally. The results of such checks should give rise to further questions, if only to hear the applicant's side of any derogatory opinions that may be expressed, since such opinions might be biased.

If the applicant is considered to be a possibility, it is useful at this stage for one of his prospective colleagues to take him on a tour of the organisation. This serves a number of purposes:

    (a) It gives both parties a rest from the strain of the interview
    (b) The opinion of the prospective colleague or colleagues should
        indicate whether he will fit in well with the existing organisation
    (c) It assists in selling the company by demonstrating good morale
    (d) It shows the applicant the environment in which he would be
        working.

Continuing the interview, the job should now be sold to the applicant. The salary and financial prospects should be stated precisely, although it must be made clear that a formal offer will be made in writing.* Professional development on the job, company training schemes, selection of personnel for promotion, pension schemes, and any other relevant matters should be discussed. If it is necessary for the applicant to move his home, he should be given information on housing, schools and local facilities.

At a convenient point in the interview the applicant's family life should be probed. This can be a delicate matter, but a man's wife can often be as much a hindrance as an asset. This is especially important in R & D, since a man with home worries cannot be expected to do good work.

APPRAISAL

It is common practice that when a new employee is appointed, his performance on the job is appraised at the end of a three month probationary period; this will confirm him or otherwise in the post. Appraisal should then be carried out regularly and if a man's work does not improve, the reasons must be uncovered and if necessary the man reassigned to make better use of his talents.

Development of a person cannot proceed without his co-operation, and perhaps the best method of obtaining this is for him to make a *self-evaluation* of his own performance. This should be followed by discussion with his superior, at the time when his performance appraisal form is being completed. It is part of a leader's duty to optimise the performance of those under his command; he must direct and encourage the motivation of the individual by guidance, providing opportunities, acknowledging improvements and rewarding. Guidance should be given in correcting self-acknowledged weaknesses, but the emphasis should be placed on

*For specific information on current salary rates, the reader is referred to the surveys carried out periodically by the professional institutions both in the United Kingdom and the United States.

providing the opportunities which will allow the individual's talents to develop; for it is in these that his maximum value to the organisation must lie.

Most organisations have standard forms for making *performance appraisals*, or, as they are sometimes called, *merit reports*. To ensure uniformity in presentation, the form may list the qualities given in the job specification, with boxes for the reporting officer to tick, marked:

(a) Outstanding
(b) Above average
(c) Average
(d) Below average
(e) Poor.

Provision should be made for amplifying the notes. Comments as to general performance, guidance given, opportunities provided, and recommendations for promotion and/or salary increase should be made by the reporting officer. In addition, he should note any illnesses or troubles the individual has incurred, as these may mark the start of a decline in a quality such as concentration or motivation; recording such information will be of help if it becomes necessary to take action.

In completing such a form, precautions must be taken by senior management to ensure that all reporting personnel have a common standard for 'average' and that no bias is caused by personalities, or the desire to maintain a *status quo*. One practical way of overcoming this is for the reporting officer to justify his marking if a general improvement has not been shown. A further check will be provided if each employee completes a self-appraisal form which, after discussion with his reporting officer, diverges from that officer's report.

MANPOWER INVENTORY

The *manpower inventory* (MI) has been defined as[4] 'a method for ensuring that the company has an opportunity to make maximum use of the skills of its personnel, and that its scientific personnel may be recognised and promoted as responsible openings occur'.

Basically, the manpower inventory must consist of a filing system such as punched cards. The attributes of each member of the staff are recorded in such a manner that, for any job specification, the names of personnel that might be suitable can be extracted. The more detailed information held in their personal file can then be examined, with a view to selection for interview. This system can aid resource allocation (see Chapter 7) although it may be desirable to place certain limitations on candidates selected; for example, a candidate might not be considered eligible until he had proved himself in his present job and had served in it for a minimum period. If a candidate is selected for promotion but cannot be released from his present position, he should be guaranteed promotion within a certain time.

It is obvious that such a system must be updated continuously and that it is complementary to the periodical appraisal report, ensuring an equitable promotion procedure. Another way in which it helps in improving staff morale is by its use in the reassignment of staff on recommendation, on their own application, or because of potential redundancy.

TRAINING

An organisation can never be static and with the increasing complexity of technical problems, a staff training programme is essential. Not only does it ensure that personnel acquire knowledge unique to the company, but also it is now recognised as an inducement for recruitment, in that it assists staff to obtain higher qualifications or to qualify for promotion. The extent of study is obviously a personal matter, but it must be company policy to encourage such effort.

Training must therefore fall into four categories:

(a) Company instruction
(b) Continuing education
(c) Training for promotion
(d) Assistance in obtaining higher or additional qualifications.

The necessity for special instruction arises principally when new staff are engaged, so that they are familiarised with:

(a) Company procedure—this will include the company organisation, aims, paperwork systems, etc.
(b) Products, processes and techniques applicable to the organisation
(c) Special equipment, for example, computers, electron microscopes.

Special instruction is also necessary to correct the mismatch between education and company requirements. Programmes for this may be extremely difficult to plan, as it involves employee motivation.[5] It has always been recognised that conferment of a degree demonstrates merely that a person has the basic knowledge of a profession; before a graduate can be considered competent in his work, he requires six to twelve months' experience, and how to speed up this process is an unsolved problem. The question of motivation arises, since he has to do what the company considers necessary and not what he would prefer. For example, the company may require something to work, whilst his preference might be to investigate why something does not work. This problem can be even more difficult when a person has high academic qualifications and little or no experience in industry.

It has been stated[6] that eight to ten hours' studying per week is necessary to avoid professional obsolescence due to loss of unused knowledge and the generation of new knowledge. The effort of keeping abreast is obviously a personal matter to the scientist or engineer, but the need to do so should be inculculated and encouraged by the company.

Fig. 3.1 shows the results of a survey carried out to determine how engineers keep up to date with their subject, but there is no information as to the relative worth of each method. The company can assist by providing adequate library facilities, paying expenses and granting leave for attending conferences, courses and possibly summer schools. The company can also co-operate with professional societies and local colleges in the preparation of suitable lectures and courses, particularly

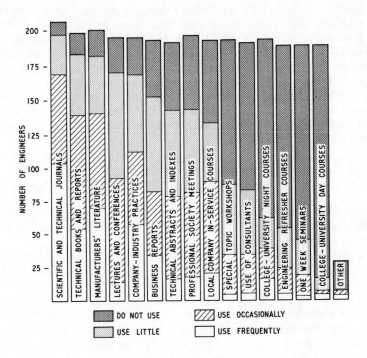

Fig. 3.1. Where engineers obtain their 'continuing education'. (Based on a survey by Pennsylvania State University.) From: 'How to avoid engineering obsolescence', EBERSOL, E. T., Electron. Ind. p. 132 October (1965). Reproduced with acknowledgement to Electronic Industries

those which meet requirements indicated by the staff themselves. In making such arrangements, the needs of senior management staff should not be forgotten, particularly if they have to handle disciplines other than their own; it may be noted that several universities in the United States now have 'cram' courses for this purpose.

Training for promotion usually means the teaching of skills required for management. This may be simply a general management course devoted to other business functions such as manufacturing, finance, sales, or, in the case of a Government department, a staff course. The curricula of such courses are usually well established by colleges, and advanced studies are often organised by firms of consultants. For promotion to particular posts, arrangements may have to be made to teach particular management skills such as operations research, systems analysis, decision theory and modern concepts of mathematics.

New recruits at the scientific assistant or laboratory technician level are expected in most organisations to undertake further training. (This has become increasingly more important since the Industrial Training Act was passed in 1964). The nature of the training varies according to where the technician is employed and the main subject with which he is concerned. In general, promotion depends on successful completion of such courses.[7] Training is usually encouraged by part time day release to local colleges, which may follow curricula set by the relevant professional society. In some organisations, selected technicians may be encouraged to graduate by being granted leave to take a sandwich course. Beyond this stage the pursuit of a higher qualification is usually left to the employee although the cost of courses may be refunded if completed successfully. It should be noted that in the United States, employers and universities often co-operate, so that an employee can prepare and submit a thesis on his actual work.

RETENTION AND SALARY ADMINISTRATION

The ability of an organisation to retain staff is often a measure of a company's growth and the opportunities this creates, rather than the result of company policy.

A survey has been carried out[8] to determine what an engineer wants from a job, and the results seem to be applicable to all scientists. The needs appear to be:

1. Programming and scheduling of his work assignments, clearly defined objectives and planning in detail
2. A set pattern to follow, but devoid of the tendency to routinise his job
3. Competent supervisors
4. Adequate credit from his company for his ideas and accomplishments
5. Security in his job—based on his attainments
6. Favourable regard of top management for his work
7. Compensation, concrete awards and economic advancement
8. Assurance that his supervisors know how well he is doing
9. Opportunity to influence work on technical projects
10. Follow through, performed by himself on the job he has started
11. Participation in the decisions which affect him
12. Opportunities to see his ideas put to use
13. Freedom to maintain an independent, self-directing attitude on how to tackle any particular problem
14. The right work assignment
15. Variety of professional work

16. Work that is challenging and stimulating
17. Planned programmes or opportunities for self development and advancement
18. Information which explains how this work fits into the entire project or product
19. Adequate facilities to get his work done
20. A well organised supporting staff and adequate technical assistance
21. Employment in a company that is known for its excellent products and reputable professional staff
22. Association with a company which clearly defines authority and responsibilities.

Summarising, this calls for an effective organisation, which permits the employee to use his discretion within reasonable bounds, and provides continuity of work. These are matters of administration and their implementation should present no difficulties.

With improvement in performance and a record of successful work, the scientist will expect economic advancement commensurate with what he considers he might get elsewhere. Salary administration is therefore of prime importance. It is common practice for each grade of effort to be placed within a *salary band*, based on surveys and studies such as those carried out by the professional societies or the Civil Service. The starting point within the grade is often a matter of negotiation; increases within the salary band may be administered by one or a combination of the following methods:

(a) *Negotiated increases.* The employee negotiates his own increase, as and when he feels able. This method does not encourage retention, as the employee may feel he is put in an invidious position
(b) *Administered compensation.* As a result of the appraisal report, the individual is awarded what he is considered to be worth to the organisation
(c) *Replacement cost.* Salaries are reviewed on the basis of what would have to be paid if an individual was replaced. Again, reliance is placed on the appraisal report
(d) *Ranking plan.* Individuals in each grade are ranked by their reporting officer in accordance with their appraisal reports, and salaries are rated accordingly
(e) *Annual increase.* An individual receives an annual increase, provided his work is satisfactory, until he reaches the top of the salary band.

Salary bands have to be reviewed periodically in relation to the cost of living differentials with skilled workers or other personnel, and the market demand. Dissatisfaction can often arise by increasing the starting salary of new graduates without changing the salary band for the established staff.

Transfer to a higher salary band should be due to promotion; it is essential that an equitable system is in operation, otherwise discontent can arise not only in staff passed over, but also in those under the new command. Promotion may carry fringe benefits such as a company car, extra holidays, better pension rights, all of which can help to retain staff.

To men with family responsibilities the security of a job is important, and it is necessary to keep them informed both of their own prospects and the long term prospects of the company. This is particularly important when they are engaged on a job with a finite life. Should business deteriorate, this procedure, by giving them the maximum time to find a new position, can avoid rancour. It is advisable, however, to have a specific policy, particularly when cancellation of contracts might occur, and where key men are concerned. Such a policy should aim at retaining the staff for some defined period before serving notice or disbanding them to other divisions of the organisation, every effort being made to find alternative work. For those staff declared redundant, *redundancy* payments may be made, based on salary and length of service; (this is mandatory in the United Kingdom). The period of notice should be commensurate with seniority.

When staff *resign*, their reasons for so doing should be recorded, and an analysis kept which may indicate possible action to prevent further resignations. In any event there should be a friendly termination procedure.

REFERENCES

1. DELLOW, F., 'Electrical engineering education in the United States of America', *Electron & Power*, **12**, p. 86, March (1966)
2. LE PAGE, *et al.*, 'A national survey of electrical engineering graduate programs', *IEEE Trans. Educ.*, **E-7**, No. 4, p. 115 (1964)
3. ZUKOWSKI, R. W., 'Planning for effective technical recruiting', *IEEE Trans. Engng. Mgmt.*, **EM-12**, No. 1, p. 22 (1965)
4. See Bibliography item No. 3
5. CLAASEN, R. S., 'Research training for the engineer', *IEEE Trans. Educ.* **E-8**, No. 1, p. 1 (1965)
6. WOLFE, J. K., 'Keeping up to date—in career training in the USA', *Electron & Power*, **11**, pp. 260, 261, 265, August (1965)
7. CHATTAWAY, F. W., 'Recruitment and career prospects for laboratory technicians', *Bull. Inst. Phys.*, **15**, No. 5, p. 110, (1964)
8. RAUDSEPP, E., 'Why engineers work', *Mach. Design*, **32**, p. 100, February 4th (1960)

BIBLIOGRAPHY

VON FANGE, E. K., *Professional Creativity*, Prentice Hall, (1959)
YODER, D., *Personnel Principles and Policies*, Prentice Hall, 2nd ed. (1959)
HEYEL, C., *Handbook of Industrial Research Management*, Reinhold Publishing Corp. (1960)
CADE, C. M., 'Qualifications for electronics', *Brit. Commun. Electron.*, **8**, No. 4, p. 254 (1961)
KARGER, D. W., MURDICK, R. G., *Managing Engineering and Research*, The Industrial Press, NY (1963)

FREIBURGHOUSE, E. H., 'Retraining for electrical engineering employees in industry', *IEEE Trans. Educ.*, **E-7** Nos. 2 & 3, p. 78–82 (1964)

WRIGHT, D. A., 'The education of physicists for industry', *Bull. Inst. Phys.*, **15**, No. 11, p. 269 (1964)

EBERSOL, E. T., 'How to avoid engineering obsolescence', *Electron. Ind.*, **24**, p. 132, October (1965)

ROACH, J. W., 'R & D categorisation: a tool for research and development management', *IEEE Trans. Aerospace & Electron. Syst.*, **AES-1**, No. 2, p. 67 (1965)

SAYLES, D. C., 'Professional obsolescence and this rapidly expanding technological era', *Nature*, **207**, No. 5001, p. 1028, (1965)

YOUNG, J., *Technicians Today and Tomorrow*, Pitman (1965)

Chapter 4

The Budgetary Process

Budgets are management's forecasts of expenditure and receipts for some specified future period. These forecasts are prepared for every division of an organisation, and integrated into a *profit and loss account* for the whole. The importance of the budget to the R & D manager lies in the *approval* of the total sum that can be made available for all projects. *Budgetary control* is the way in which management exercises control by the constant examination of the variances arising between the actual results and those predicted.

BUDGETS AND ESTIMATES

Budgeted and estimated costs may be, but are not necessarily, synonymous. In this book, an estimate is defined as the planned effort and costs of a particular project or part of a project, from its conception, or some later stage, to completion. By a budget is meant the statement of resources required over a specified period of time to implement the declared management policy. In general, an estimate is independent of other estimates, but a budget correlates all the estimates over the specified period and may be interrelated with the budgets of other divisions.

THE BUDGETARY PROCESS

The interrelationship of budgets may best be understood by considering the procedure for the preparation of budgets in a manufacturing organisation. This is depicted in Fig. 4.1.

The major step is to forecast what is termed the *principal budget factor*—that consideration which limits all aspects of the organisation, for example, the availability of capital, the production capacity, the expected sales, or the lack of trained staff. To determine this factor, it may be necessary for each department to prepare draft budgets independent of the possible limitations of other departments and based solely on

42

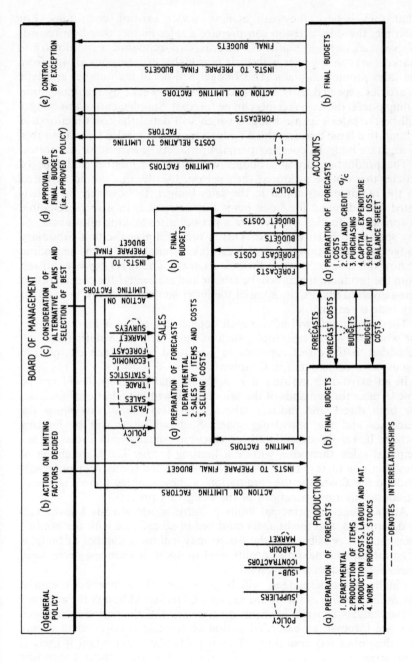

Fig. 4.1. Typical procedure for the preparation of a manufacturing budget

what they believe they can achieve under existing conditions. For example, the sales division can prepare a sales budget based on records of past sales, trade statistics, forecasts of economic conditions and market surveys, together with their reasonable expectations arising from the sales promotion plans. This budget will detail the number and type of articles expected to be sold each month or week; by recommending selling prices, the cash receipts can be forecast. Supplementing this budget will be the sales expense budget, which will detail the costs incurred in selling. In a large business these budgets may be compiled from a number of separate budgets, covering perhaps products, salesmen, or territories.

The production division budget will show the number and type of articles that can be produced each period. Ideally, this should be based on the requirements stated in the sales budget. If, however, the anticipated sales demand for stock items fluctuates, it is probably preferable to spread production evenly over a period, after making allowances for any special products expected. This in turn will give rise to a subsidiary budget of *work in progress*, which can take a number of forms depending on how this item is shown in the *balance sheet*. The *direct expenses* arising from the production plan will be labour and materials, due consideration being given to the provisioning of the latter so that the 'stock in hand' at any time is reasonable.

The accountants will advise each department of the *indirect expenses* for which they are responsible, such as rent, fuel, office staff; these will be added to the direct expenses to give total costs. (Such charges are discussed in more detail in Chapter 6.)

In an expanding industry it is probable that production will not be able to meet the demands of the sales budget without additional facilities for both direct and indirect labour, and also *capital investment* for machines and manufacturing space. Such additions will be limiting factors. If, on the other hand, production capacity is in excess of anticipated sales, then sales will be a limiting factor. The highlighting of these limiting factors by the management and the subsequent proposals made to the Board for the elimination of these limiting factors is one of the most important functions of the budgetary process.

At this stage the principal limiting factor, if not already known, can be determined, and the budgets modified in accordance with the Board's decision. It is possible that the Board may call for a number of budgets in an attempt to maximise profits, and to assist this process *operational research* techniques may be used.

Finally, a set of budgets will be approved which in effect comprise the *declared policy* of the Board in financial terms. Although the accuracy of the budgets depends inversely on the extent of the period over which they are forecast, an extended period of forecast is required to ensure that the policy has continuity. This is particularly important if there is long term capital investment. A compromise over these conflicting demands can be made by the simultaneous preparation of a long term budget of perhaps five years, with a more accurate budget for the forthcoming year. The long term budget will be a revised version of that of the previous year, depending on the policy changes made during the year; the short term budget must fall within the long term one.

BUDGETARY CONTROL

Since budgets are forecasts, it must be borne in mind that assumptions will have been made and that the actual costs when available may show deviations. In a manufacturing organisation, the outcomes from certain inputs can be related and estimated with reasonable accuracy, and control can be exercised from the variances that will arise. Furthermore, in a manufacturing organisation, the prime purpose of budgetary control is to establish control of expenditure and ensure that it corresponds to the provisions made, so that finally the desired profit is achieved.

R & D BUDGETS

The method of preparation of an R & D budget is similar to that described for manufacturing,[1] except that the limiting factors are normally known in advance. These are most likely to be:

(a) Availability of finance
(b) Availability of skilled manpower
(c) Ability of the company to produce and market new products envisaged.

The budget must be based on the programme of R & D work planned,[2] which will fall into certain categories:

(a) *Standing orders*—for technical support to operating divisions:
　1. Technical assistance to production
　2. Technical assistance to sales
　3. Competitive product study
　4. Patent study
　5. Library
(b) *Special orders*—anticipated, such as:
　1. Work of a similar nature to that covered by a standing order, but sufficiently large in scope to be accounted for separately
　2. Feasibility studies
(c) *Project orders*—that is, work already authorised and continuing:
　1. Private venture
　2. Under contract for customers. (Provision for overspending may have to be made)
(d) *New R & D work envisaged:*
　1. Private venture
　2. Under contract for customers.

(It should be noted that expenditure on 'standing orders' and feasibility studies may be charged to overheads.)

The programme will be the basis of the *manpower, financial,* and *capital budgets,* hence it must be supported by estimates. For the first

45

| | ANNUAL BUDGET—
SUMMARY OF PERSONNEL, WAGES & SALARIES | | | | | | | Location | | | |

	STAFF AS AT										
	Personnel		4 Weeks Basic Wage			Over- time	TOTAL WAGES & SALS.	1		2	
	M	F	Hourly	Weekly	4-Wkly.			M	F	M	
DIRECT Engineering											
Drawing Office											
Model Shop											
TOTAL DIRECT											
INDIRECT Administration											

PERIOD			1	2	3	4	5

	M	F	M	F	M	F	M	F	M	F
PERSONNEL STRENGTH—Direct										
PERSONNEL STRENGTH—Indirect										

DIRECT WAGES & SALARIES Engineering					
Drawing Office					
Model Shop					
TOTAL DIRECT WAGES & SALARIES					
HIRED LABOUR					
INDIRECT WAGES & SALARIES Indirect Personnel					
Indirect Bookings: Engineering					
Drawing Office					
Model Shop					
Holiday Pay Reserve					
TOTAL INDIRECT WAGES & SALARIES					

Fig. 4.2. A typical ann

Division	Year	Issue	Date	Department
				ENGINEERING

PERSONNEL CHANGES

3		4		5		6		7		8		9		10		11		12		13	
F	M	F	M	F	M	F	M	F	M	F	M	F	M	F	M	F	M	F	M	F	M	F

6		7		8		9		10		11		12		13		Annual Budget
F	M	F	M	F	M	F	M	F	M	F	M	F	M	F	M	F

power budget

item, that is the various standing orders, records of the previous year's expenditure, considered in conjunction with both production and sales plans, should give a fairly accurate forecast of requirements. For the project orders already authorised and continuing, up to date detailed estimates should be available. For the remaining two items (special orders and new work envisaged) provision has to be made in accordance with the known policy of the company.

For the budget to be soundly based, the objectives of the company must give the required rate of growth in such terms as sales, profits, or share of the market. From this, the research manager must build up his programme on the basis of: (a) those projects which are necessary to the further development of existing products; and (b) the establishment of new products, taking into account the potential profitability of each so as to achieve the required rate of growth. At the same time he must consider the research effort needed in each case, and the probability of success. This process is described more fully in Chapter 5.

The programme will need to be converted into manpower requirements both in qualitative and quantitative terms. This will indicate the need for further recruitment, and will also reveal areas of skill not utilised fully, which in turn may affect the programme. The core of this budget must, therefore, be the scheduling and allocation of resources to the various projects. (This is discussed in detail in Chapter 7.) An example of a manpower budget is shown in Fig. 4.2.

The financial budget will express the overall projected costs of the research establishment in terms of budgeted labour, material and overhead requirements. It will also reflect the method of financing the work, which may be:

(a) Offload of expenditure to manufacturing or product group
(b) Recoveries as a percentage of the cost build up of products sold
(c) Payments from contractors
(d) Private investment, i.e. company finance
(e) Revenue from pilot plant production
(f) Credits for royalty income and patent rights sold.

A capital budget will be submitted in respect of:

(a) Additions or extensions to buildings, plant, research equipment, and general facilities
(b) Pilot plant requirements for particular projects
(c) Equipment and facilities for additional personnel to be recruited under the manpower budget.

In an R & D laboratory, the continued employment of trained staff will provide a relatively stable cost, and any increases in the budget from the previous year will be due to:

(a) Salary increases
(b) Provision of extra facilities
(c) Expansion of staff
(d) Increase in overheads.

The increase in the cost of research has averaged about 4% p.a. over the years 1960 to 1965 in both the United Kingdom and the United States.

As the output from a laboratory cannot be determined accurately in financial terms, budget variance cannot be used for control, and this gives rise to some differences between R & D and operational budgets:

(a) As long as the research proves satisfactory, there is a tendency for the R & D manager to increase his requests, particularly if the company is profitable

(b) The budget may be tailored to what the manager considers the Board expects

(c) The budget will not demonstrate the effectiveness or otherwise of the R & D.

BUDGET APPROVAL

The Board must consider the R & D budget in association with all other budgets to ensure that the resources will be available to meet the commitments that arise. Any increase in the budget from previous years must be assessed on the basis of whether the money would pay a higher return if it was invested elsewhere. This is of particular importance, as any increase in effect commits the company to the higher expenditure for future years, R & D being a continuous process which cannot proceed successfully on a stop-go basis. Such influences will tend to be deflationary, but opposing them will be the long term financial policy towards growth, and necessity to maintain leadership in those fields set out in the company's objectives.

The adequacy of the budget will most probably be reviewed against the known level of those of competitors, a long hard look being taken as to whether the R & D is equally as effective. Attempts have been made, with varying degrees of success, to systematise testing for the adequacy or otherwise of the budget. The methods used fall into one of three groups:

(a) *Relationships and trends.*[3, 4] Companies often have their own general tests based on a ratio of the R & D budget to either profit or total sales. Such ratios are generally considered useful when taken in conjunction with historical data, and for comparing expenditure with that of competitors

(b) *Financial methods*—examples of which are:

1. *Reserve computation*[5]

   Let R = gross R & D costs

   $R/2$ = net R & D costs, assuming a 50% tax rate

   P = gross new investment in plant

   W = required working capital

   S = expected annual sales volume of new products

   N = minimum acceptable profit as a percentage of sales

   Y = company's maximum allowed payback period for investments.

Equating the gross investment in plant, working capital, and R & D, with the expected annual profits by the number of years in the payback period:

$$P + W + R/2 = YSN$$

i.e. $$R = 2(YSN - P - W)$$

This formula is considered best for checking the adequacy of development or applied research costs, since at this stage the factors, which are those used in capital budgeting techniques, can be estimated with some degree of accuracy.

2. *Return on investment*[6]

Let P = expected profit before any R & D costs
I = total investment
R = desired rate of return on investment, then:

$$P - (R \& D \text{ costs}) = RI$$

i.e. $(R \& D \text{ costs}) = P - RI$

The above methods can only be guidelines, since they do not take into account the probability of success or the net return of the proposed investment. For these reasons the financial aspects of all major projects should be analysed separately as described in Chapter 5.

(c) *Operational research.* It is beyond the scope of this book to describe the mathematical models that have been derived; a good example, however, is given in reference 7.

Since the effective direction of the R & D policy by the Board can only be maintained by approval of the programme and control of finances, the Board will:

(a) Authorise the budget *in toto*, giving the research director complete freedom of action within specified broad fields, perhaps with an indication of the finance to be spent in certain areas

(b) Give general approval to the overall expenditure projects, but subject major projects to specific consideration and approval as they mature during the year.

CONCLUSION

The interrelationships between the departmental budgets of an organisation have been shown. The major difference in an R & D budget is that, being discretionary, it cannot be used for control purposes, nor does it demonstrate the efficiency of the department. It is only, in fact, the supporting evidence for an annual appropriation, based on the desirable and profitable proposed research projects and made within the confines of some known limiting factor, such as finance or effort. Because of this, it tends to remain relatively constant until such time as the Board is convinced that the level of effort is inadequate to support the company's policy. Although the argument has been based on industrial practice, there will be similar consideration in a Government or non-profit making organisation.

The chief benefits accruing from an R & D budget lie in the achievement of a balanced programme of work, and the co-ordination of this programme with those of other sections of the organisation.

REFERENCES

1. ANTHONY, R. N., *Management Controls in Industrial Research Organisations*, Harvard Univ. Press (1952)
2. SOUTHALL, H. P., *The Management Accountant's Influence on Research & Development*, The Institute of Cost & Works Accountants, Summer School (1961)
3. DEAN B. V., SENQUPTA, S. S., 'Research budgeting and project selection', *IRE Trans. Engng. Mgmt.*, **EM-9**, No. 4, p. 158 (1962)
4. SEEBER, N. C., 'Decision making on research and development in the business firm' *National Science Foundation Bulletin* 44, Feb. (1964)
5. MANLEY, R. H., 'Translating economic aspects of company policy into research policy', *5th Ann. Conf. Ind. Res.*, Columbia University, USA (1954)
6. VILLERS, R., *Research & Development: Planning and Control*, Financial Executives Research Foundation Inc., NY (1964)
7. DEAN, B. V., SENQUPTA, S. S., 'On a method for determining corporate research budgets', *Management Sciences, Models and Techniques*, (Eds.: Churchman, C. W., Verhulst, M) **2**, p. 210, Pergamon Press (1960)

BIBLIOGRAPHY

ELBOURNE, E. T., *Fundamentals of Industrial Administration*, **1** and **2**, Macdonald & Evans (1934), (1942)
WILLSMORE, A. W., *Business Budgets & Budgetary Control*, Pitman, 4th edit. (1960)
MORANIAN, J., *The Research & Development Engineer as a Manager*, Rutgens, The State University, Holt Rinehart & Winston (1963)
SEILER, R. E., *Improving the Effectiveness of Research & Development*, McGraw-Hill (1965)
HOWARD, G. W., *Common Sense in Research & Development Management*, Vintage Books Inc., NY (1955)
QUINN, J. B., *How Industry uses R & D Budgets*, The Management Review, American Management Assoc. Inc. NY (1959)
MILTON, H. S., *Cost-of-Research Index, 1920–1965*, Research Analysis Corporation, Mclean, Virginia (1966)

Chapter 5

The R & D Programme

In defining the administration problem (Chapter 1), the spectrum of work, both creative and non-creative, and the responsibility for preparing a programme were discussed. The success of an R & D laboratory will depend on its creative function and will be assessed by the contribution this makes to increasing the capability of the parent organisation. Hence the programme must be prepared, and evaluated periodically for maximum effectiveness, particularly as the effort and finance available is always a limiting factor.

The creative programme may be sub-divided into broad areas:

(a) *State of the art investigations.* This may extend from keeping a watching brief—through experimentation to find possible applications—to pure basic research

(b) *Projects*—that is, all the work relating to the research and development of a new product or process independent of any other project. In the initial stages this may be limited to a feasibility study, the publication of a report, or the allocation of a check point; that is, a point where the work will be reviewed before approval is given to continue.

The preparation of the programme must follow various stages:

(a) Reviews of existing work
(b) Screening of ideas
(c) Formulation of proposals
(d) Selection of:
   1. Alternative proposals, i.e. having the same objective
   2. Different proposals.

The selection process may depend on the qualitative judgement of individuals, although the trend is now towards a quantitative approach. In any event, all stages should be formalised to ensure a sufficient depth of thought. The importance of this lies in the fact that, as with all R & D work, forecasting cannot be accurate. Programming must therefore be dynamic, so that it can change in accordance with the execution of the plan. Unless careful consideration is given to the preparation of the programme, its execution will be bedevilled with the introduction of crash projects.

SCREENING OF IDEAS

To encourage the formulation and declaration of new ideas, it is necessary that they should be appraised impartially and moreover, should be seen to be appraised impartially. This is important because, on average, only about half of the ideas put forward can be expected to result in approved proposals. Surveys have shown that the sources for ideas are:

Research staff members	60%
Marketing and sales staff	17%
Customers, including Government agencies	9%
Management	9%
Other, e.g. production and engineering, personnel, consultants, universities.	5%

An initial screening may be done by the director of research, chief scientist, or other person, to determine primarily that the idea is acceptable with reference to the declared policy. If acceptable, the technical implications can be examined by the R & D staff to enable the 'promise of success' to be assessed. By this is meant, not only the probability of success, but also the adequacy of the existing organisation and facilities to reach a solution. If the idea appears sufficiently important, the report can be qualified to show how the promise of success can be improved.

At this stage the appraisal authority may reject the idea, but it is important that he does not do this solely on the grounds of a low probability of success; other factors, particularly a possible high rate of return, can warrant further consideration.

The detailed evaluation of an idea must take into account many factors, the extent and weighting of which will depend on the organisation. Table 5.1 gives a guide which indicates how complex the problem may be and illustrates the necessity for a systematic method. However, the expenditure required to gather the information can be considerable and therefore a 'first pass' may be done, perhaps by a committee, to decide whether the idea is worthy of the full procedure.

THE PROPOSAL

'Selection' presupposes the existence of alternatives. For the best decision to be made, there must be sufficient depth of thought and the information should be collated in such a way that it aids comparison; furthermore, departments other than R & D are usually involved to advise on finance, production, marketing, patents, etc., and other divisons may have to be informed. It is therefore necessary to have a procedure, with which may be associated a standard form, the documents usually being termed the *proposal* or *application*. After approval by the Board this becomes the authority by which the R & D director can authorise work. An example of a standard form which accompanies supporting documents is given in Fig. 5.1(a), (b), (c) and (d). An organisation may periodically approve a *blanket proposal*, to give the necessary cover for small projects which are left to the discretion of

Table 5.1. FACTORS TO BE CONSIDERED IN PROJECT SELECTION

Technical factors	1. Availability of the necessary scientific skills 2. Adequacy of research facilities (need for employing consultants, research associations, etc.) 3. Adequacy of support manpower 4. Utilisation of present skills 5. Probability of technical success 6. Technical approach required to reach a solution
Research direction and balance	1. Compatibility of company objectives 2. Compatibility of long term research objectives 3. Maintenance of research balance by products 4. Maintenance of balance between the intermediate and long range introduction of new products
Timing of research	1. Timing of research completion 2. Timing of development completion 3. Timing of market development 4. Timing of research in relation to competitors' efforts
Stability	1. Prominence of the market 2. Possibility of a captive market 3. Stability in a depression 4. Stability in time of war or shifts in defence spending 5. Difficulty of substitution or copying
Position factor	1. Effect on the sales of other product lines 2. Effect on vertical or horizontal integration resulting from raw material usage 3. Possibility of an exclusive raw material purchasing position
Growth factors	1. Export possibilities 2. Possibility of changes or shifts in the industry of which this product can take advantage 3. Possibility of a family of products growing from the research 4. Possibility of substantial future growth in size 5. Diversification

Marketability factor	1. Market potential in immediate future 2. Market potential in long range future 3. Compatibility with current and long range marketing objectives 4. Competitive environment 5. Promotional requirements 6. Adaptability to present distribution methodology and resources 7. Volume price effects on present products 8. Relationship to Governmental legislation 9. Compatibility with company's present customer make-up 10. Service requirements for product guarantee or upkeep 11. Variations of styles required 12. Compatibility with the company's present reputation in the market
Production factors	1. Compatibilities of production facilities 2. Utilisation of familiar production processes 3. Freedom from hazards 4. Availability of manpower
Financial factors	1. Expected increase in profits 2. Expected new capital outlays for equipment 3. Expected cost to complete the project 4. Expected cost to complete the development 5. Expected cost to manufacture 6. Expected rate of return on invested capital
Protection	1. Possibility of a patent 2. Unique character of the product or process 3. Need for continuing defensive research in respect of known areas of competitors' work

*From *Improving the Effectiveness of Research and Development* by SEILER, R. E., Copyright 1965, McGraw-Hill Book Company. Used by permission.

the R & D director or manager, although in other companies such approval may be part of the budgetary process.

The scope and the extent of the proposal must reflect the size of the project. At the minimum, it should give the *requirement specification*, the proposed planning and scheduling and detailed estimates, the compilation of which is discussed in Chapters 6 and 7. It should also include justification for the work and the background knowledge.

The justification of a project rarely lies solely with R & D staff, since it may be concerned primarily with marketing or other factors, and the financial matters arising. The justification must firstly, show that the project has an objective that will promote the policy of the company; secondly, show how the financial investment may be recovered; and thirdly, indicate the potential benefits or profits. The determination of the last two factors gives rise to the need for a *business analysis*, which will include *a market survey* if a new product is envisaged.

55

DEVELOPMENT ORDER

APPLICATION FOR AUTHORISATION OF PRIVATE VENTURE
RESEARCH AND DEVELOPMENT EXPENDITURE

ORDER NUMBER

ᴅ P D

TITLE

GROUP

DIVISION

DEPARTMENT

PRODUCT AREA No.

SUBMISSION NUMBER.............................

DATE OF ORIGINATION..........................

PRODUCT ANALYSIS NUMBER

PA

TO BE COMPLETED FOR ALL **D** ORDE
EXCEPT WHEN MORE THAN ONE PRODU
IS INVOLVED IN WHICH CASE INDIVIDU
ENGINEERING ORDERS WILL BE ALLOCAT
PA NUMBERS ENTERED ON PAGE 4.

Amend. No.	Cumulative Amount Requested for this Application £	Completion Date for this Application	Estimated Total Cost of this Order to Production Stage £	Requested by : (Head of Dept.)	SUPPORTING DETAILS CHECKED & APPROVED BY:			Date of Authorisation	Cumulative Authorised Cover for this Application £	Application Approved Group Director
					Accounts	Sales	Manager			
Original										
1										
2										
3										
4										
5										
6										
7										

SPECIAL INSTRUCTIONS

F 3566

(a)

Fig. 5.1. (a), (b), (c), (d). A standard form for obt.

DESCRIPTION OF WORK COVERED BY THIS APPLICATION

DESCRIPTION OF ANY PREVIOUS WORK RELATED TO THIS PROJECT
(STATE ALSO ORDER Nos. AND EXPENDITURES)

oval for an R & D project (continued overleaf)

(b)

POTENTIAL

GRAND TOTAL ESTIMATED PD DEVELOPMENT COST TO PRODUCTION STAGE INCL. RELEVANT EXPENDITURE NOT ON THIS ORDER	SALES FORECAST (X £1,000)						ESTIMATED BREAK EVEN DATE	EXPENDITURE ON THIS CATEGORY OF WORK PRIOR TO THIS ORDER	AMO ALRE RECO\
	PRIOR TO 19 /	19 /	19 /	19 /	19 /	19 /		£	£
£									

SPECIFICATION

IS SPECIFICATION AVAILABLE? ....

SPECIFICATION NUMBER.................................

DOES SPECIFICATION
INCLUDE TARGET
WORKS COST? ....

COMMENT

FINANCIAL

IS THIS PROJECT
STATED IN THE BUDGET?..........................

IF YES STATE B/3 ITEM No. ....

WILL AUTHORISATION OF THIS
APPLICATION RESULT IN TOTAL
DPD COVER FOR THIS YEAR
EXCEEDING TOTAL DPD BUDGET? ....

WILL BUDGET ITEM BE
EXCEEDED? ....

COMMENT

GENERAL

DOES PROJECT RENDER ANY
EXISTING PRODUCT OBSOLETE?

WILL SALES OF ANY EXISTING
PRODUCTS BE AIDED?

WILL ANY SPECIAL ACTION BE NEEDED?
  (i.e. Samples, Demonstrations, Trials, Installation Service)

VALUE OF TOOLS, TESTGEAR AND PLANT
INCLUDED IN THIS APPLICATION   £

VALUE OF TOOLS, TESTGEAR & PLANT REQUIRED
NOT INCLUDED IN THIS APPLICATION   £

WILL ANY SPECIAL APPROVAL BE NEEDED?
  (i.e. E.I.D., A.R.B., etc.)

PATENT LICENCE SITUATION

COMPETITION

IS TECHNICAL EFFORT AVAILABLE?
IF NOT STATE PROPOSED ACTION

IS ADDITIONAL FLOOR SPACE REQUIRED?
IF YES, STATE PROPOSED ACTION

(c)

LIST OF ENGINEERING ORDERS

(SUBSIDIARY TO THIS
DEVELOPMENT ORDER
ISSUED WITHIN OWN
DEPT.)

RDER No.	PRODUCT ANALYSIS FORM NUMBER (WHEN NOT ON PAGE 1 OF THIS FORM)	TITLE	COVER £

CLOSURE

REASON FOR CLOSURE

REQUESTED BY HEAD OF DEPT.........................DATE....................

CLOSURE AGREED					CLOSURE APPROVED
	SALES	PRODUCTION	ACCOUNTS		MANAGER
					DATE

FINAL COSTS £

Fig. 5.1. continued

(d)

BUSINESS ANALYSIS

In R & D when the results lie in the future, a business analysis can only be arrived at by extrapolating trends and making logical deductions from technological, economic, sociological (including defence) and other requirements; these, in turn, are determined from numerous sources of information. (Government publications are the source of most statistical information, and much information of relevance to R & D is published in the United States by the National Science Foundation.) It is rare for the R & D worker to have the time or inclination to investigate these sources, and in any event his enthusiasm for an idea may colour his outlook, a risk that should not be taken when R & D is so costly. Neither can this be considered a commercial function, since a good understanding of the scientific principles are necessary. For these reasons most organisations, including Government departments, have within their peripheral support, specialists who are responsible for drawing up the proposal, and who report to top management.

The starting point of the analysis must be to determine and confirm all possible applications of the end result. This process may generate feedback and may result in modifications to the requirement specification. At the same time, this active searching and study should guide the research workers to those broad areas of requirements where there are still problems to be solved. They are perhaps awaiting some fundamental or technological advance and this is a most important consideration in the overall guidance of research work.

With the applications defined, it may be possible to make a market survey, even if there is no product or process to demonstrate. It is then the job of the market researcher to determine the best sources of information and to continue investigating these until he has sufficient facts on the potential market and competition to submit to the management. The sources of such information can be:

(a) Customers and business contacts
(b) Company employees
(c) Government departments
(d) Trade associations
(e) Technical conferences and symposia
(f) Professional publications
(g) Government publications, including reports
(h) Business and financial publications
(i) Trade exhibitions
(j) Competitors' catalogues and promotional material
(k) Consultants.

In addition to supplying the supporting evidence for a proposal, the market survey will be the basis of the *sales forecast*, which must include recommendations as to the strategic completion date of development. This forecast will also reflect on the R & D budget, particularly if contracts may be obtained from Government departments or other contractors. It should be noted, however, that such possibilities should be appraised realistically, particularly with regard to the time required to negotiate a contract.

SELECTION

The essential elements of any selection process are:

(a) Objective
(b) Alternative methods of achieving the objective
(c) Relevant information on each alternative, e.g. cost, promise of success
(d) Forecast of expected conditions. In cost effectiveness analysis, and other operational research methods, a mathematical or logical model may be used
(e) A criterion for choosing the preferred alternative.

The criterion, and therefore the method, of selection must depend on the stated objective. If the objective is confined to the development of a specific product or process, the alternative proposals may not differ widely in concept. The criteria may then be limited to the degree of product or process improvement that may be expected, with the estimated cost of achieving this improvement. The best concept of objective is probably that used in *cost effectiveness analysis*, where it is defined as: 'the real functional needs underlying a specified requirement'. Only the examination of such needs, by disclosing the fundamental problem, can justify a basic research programme which may not mature for years, whilst it may also generate new ideas through the systematic exploration of all feasible alternatives.

In an industrial laboratory the objective is usually to maximise the return on the investment, but this may be modified in certain areas for the following reasons:

(a) The need to keep to the forefront in a particular field
(b) The necessity for attracting Government support
(c) The publicity value
(d) The knowledge that competitors are engaged on certain lines of work.

For quantitative methods of selection, a mathematical or logical model is necessary to simulate expected conditions, the outcome of which, according to the values assigned to the variables, will forecast results; depending on the validity of the model, the significant components and relationships will be identifiable, and this will be of help in making a correct decision. In R & D, such a model must be *probabilistic*, as opposed to *deterministic* (exact), and may therefore be of limited value. Nevertheless, such methods are used by certain companies who tend to keep their formulae highly confidential. The formulae are derived principally from operational research techniques, by cost effectiveness

61

analysis, or by economic methods similar to the discounted cash flow (see p. 64), modified to take into account the probability of success, the amount and period of investment and the expected recovery.

COST EFFECTIVENESS ANALYSIS

Cost effectiveness analysis is a method of studying how to make the best of several choices. It is the ratio between the ability needed to attain a certain objective (effectiveness) and the resources required to achieve this ability (cost). The term is always used in relation to the effectiveness of alternative systems.

Cost effectiveness analysis is primarily a military study, although its principles may be utilised whenever a decision has to be based on incomplete quantitative data. The purpose of this analysis is to quantify what can be calculated logically; the decision maker then knows the extent to which intuitive judgement must be used in making the decision. Assumptions about both facts and data, although of questionable validity may be made to determine how they affect the final results.

For the purpose of the analysis, cost estimates, which need not be precise, are the *net costs* or *incremental costs*; that is, the total costs from the concept of the project until the end of its operational life. This can include items such as capital investment for production, training of staff, marketing and other factors which are often not considered till a late stage. Cost estimates may be tested by a *sensitivity analysis*, a repetitive process using different values of item cost and expenditure period to determine if the results are sensitive to the values assigned, and to indicate to the decision maker the risks arising from the inaccuracies of the cost estimates.

The selection process may be made in one of two ways:

(a) Equal cost—that alternative which gives the greatest effectiveness for the same expenditure
(b) Equal effectiveness—that alternative which gives the required effectiveness at the least cost.

A third method may be used when the effectiveness cannot be forecast, for example with the introduction of a new technology. This is termed the 'incremental effectiveness at incremental cost', and seeks to relate the increase in effectiveness achieved, to the associated increase in costs involved.

RANKING METHODS

The difficulty of applying quantitative methods, especially when a large number of proposals are involved, gives rise to *selection by ranking,* either as a means or ancillary to the qualitative or subjective judgement of the R & D director.

The success of a ranking system depends on the choice of factors. It is preferable to keep the number of factors small, since this minimises the degree of freedom and therefore the inaccuracies. Only factors to which the objective is sensitive should be considered. The factors should, if possible, be the subject of quantitative measurement, since guesswork can introduce cumulative errors. For example with eight factors, and a probability of 60% that each best guess was right, the probability that all guesses are right is less than 2%.

These criteria indicate that only a judicious selection of the factors listed in Table 5.1 should be utilised, although much, if not all, of the information should be available in the proposal. It is also essential that the choice of factors is not immutable, so that the areas of priority can be re-examined[1] continually and the potential of projects is not exaggerated. One factor that must always be included is the *market gain*, even if the R & D is being paid for by a customer.

The simplest method of ranking is the *preferential matrix*. In this, each alternative is ordered, e.g. 1st, 2nd, . . . nth, for each factor, and the preferred alternatives will be those with the lowest total of ratings. A variation of this method reduces the effects of incorrect ordering; factors are given the rating of high, medium, or low, with which the values of 3, 2 and 1 are associated, and the alternatives are ranked according to the products of their ratings. The application of this method has been described,[2] using five factors:

(a) Promise of success
(b) Time to completion
(c) Cost of project
(d) Strategic need
(e) Market gain.

On evaluation, projects are ordered in descending scores, the highest possible being 3^5 (243), the lowest 1, and the individual and cumulative costs shown, so that the budget total gives the reject point.

Factors may be *weighted*, the weighting depending on the characteristics of the company. A systematic way of doing this[3] is known as the *Churchill-Ackoff scale*; in this, the factors are listed in order of importance, the most important given a weighting of unity, and the others some fraction. The alternatives are then ordered inversely for each factor and the order number multiplied by the weighting to give the rating; each rating is summed to give the preferential positions in order of highest to lowest scores.

When the factors are specified parameters, given in a clearly defined specification, the *weighted order probability scale* may be used. This is a variation of the Churchill-Ackoff scale where the probability of reaching the specified parameter, that is, the promise of success, is given instead of an order number. (The concept of an *expected achievement factor*, discussed in Chapter 8, could be used in this technique. It would have the advantage of taking into account expenditure and competence, upon which the assessment of probability depends.) A further refinement is the *weighted specification reference scale*,[4] which differs from the Churchill-Ackoff technique in that the sum of all the weighting factors is made equal to unity. Quantitative data are introduced by estimating or otherwise calculating the expected value for each alternative and expressing it as a fraction of the desired specification value.

INVESTMENTS APPRAISAL

If a market survey shows that possible receipts can be forecast as a result of R & D expenditure, the expenditure may be treated as an investment. Since the purpose of an investment is to generate receipts in excess of the amount expended, and since expenditure and receipts can vary both in amount and time, a yardstick is necessary for evaluation.

If an investment is made today, then the total gain that will be made in the future can be expressed as an average rate of compound interest. This rate is called the *rate of return*. The future worth of an investment may then be obtained from the following formula:

$$\text{Future worth} = R \times (1+i)^n$$

where R = rate of return
i = compound interest rate
n = number of years

Conversely, the present worth or value of money invested or received in the future is obtained from:

$$\text{Present worth} = R \times \frac{1}{(1+i)^n}$$

It follows that all expenditure and receipts can be converted to present worth, and a rate of return determined that will make them equal. This determination has been simplified by the *profitability index* approach which uses pretabulated work sheets and a graphic interpolation as shown in Fig. 5.2. This approach is identical in principle to that known as discounted cash flow, but in each case slightly different assumptions are made. In the example given of profitability index, the present value factors have been adjusted on the basis of:

(a) Uniform income during the year
(b) Continuous compounding of interest.

Furthermore, this technique is only valid when all investment expenditures are scheduled to be incurred prior to receipts (as usually occurs in R & D), since it builds in the assumption of the reinvestment of prior receipts at the solution interest rate. The technique may, however, be modified to overcome this error.

The profitability index technique also requires modification if it is used as a decision making process in the evaluation of two mutually exclusive proposals for business analysis; the established cost of the capital required must be taken into account in considering the differences. It is beyond the scope of this book to discuss such complications, but it

PROJECT EVALUATION SHEET

TIMING			TRIAL #1 0% INT. RATE	TRIAL #2 10% INTEREST RATE		TRIAL #3 25% INTEREST RATE		TRIAL #4 40% INTEREST RATE	
CAL. YEAR	PERIOD		ACTUAL AMOUNT OF DISBURSEMENTS	FACTOR	PRESENT WORTH	FACTOR	PRESENT WORTH	FACTOR	PRESENT WORTH
BEFORE	1st YR	AT ST	1000	1·11	1110	1·28	1280	1·49	1490
		DURING		1·05		1·14		1·23	
AFTER	1st YR	AT ST	800	1·00	800	1·00	800	1·00	800
		DURING		·95		·89		·82	
TOTALS (A)			**1800**		**1910**		**2080**		**2290**

CAL. YEAR	PERIOD		ACTUAL AMOUNT OF RECEIPTS	FACTOR	PRESENT WORTH	FACTOR	PRESENT WORTH	FACTOR	PRESENT WORTH
BEFORE	1st YEAR DURING		500	·95	475	·89	445	·82	410
	2nd " "		1000	·86	860	·69	690	·55	550
	3rd " "			·78		·54		·37	
	4th " "			·71		·42		·25	
	5th " "			·64		·33		·17	
	6th " "			·58		·25		·11	
	7th " "			·52		·20		·07	
	8th " "			·47		·15		·05	
	9th " "			·43		·12		·03	
	10th " "		3000	·39	1170	·09	270	·02	60
	11th " "			·35		·07		·02	
	12th " "			·32		·06		·01	
	13th " "			·29		·04		·01	
	14th " "			·26		·03		·01	
	15th " "			·24		·03			
	16th " "			·21		·02			
	17th " "			·19		·02			
	18th " "			·17		·01			
	19th " "			·16		·01			
	20th " "			·14		·01			
TOTALS (B)			**4500**		**2505**		**1405**		**1020**
RATIO A/B			**·40**		**·76**		**1·48**		**2·24**

(left margin labels: BEFORE ZERO POINT / AFTER ZERO POINT)

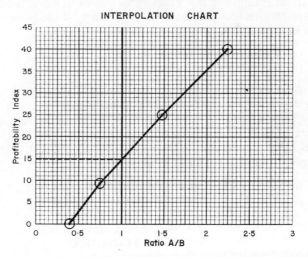

INTERPOLATION CHART

Fig. 5.2. The profitability index approach, used for investment appraisal. Reprinted from 'Capital investment and the profitability index', REUL, R., The Manager, November 1962. Courtesy: The British Institute of Management

should be self-evident how an alteration in the pattern of expenditure, even without increased expenditure, could change a profitable project into an unprofitable one.

PROJECT REVIEW

During the life of a project, the factors on which its approval was based must be reappraised continually. These must include:

(a) Promise of success
(b) Expenditure to completion
(c) Revised business analysis.

Considering the last factor, in the extreme there is no point in developing a perfect product if the market has disappeared. In practice, changes will probably arise from competition and economic factors.

If work has not yet, or only just, started no change is likely in either the probability of success or the estimate, but nevertheless a check should be made.

With work in progress, a more detailed examination is necessary, and this should include:

(a) Progress to date—achievement versus plan
(b) Technical difficulties arising
(c) Appraisal of new approaches and remedies
(d) Anticipated delays, that is a revised estimate
(e) Evaluation of work remaining in terms of the estimate.

(This is discussed more fully in Chapter 8.)

In carrying out this examination, it must be appreciated that there may be a lack of information, particularly if the project is going badly, as the research worker may consider:

(a) Failure reflects on his ability
(b) The problem will be resolved.

A *cut-off decision* must be considered if the promise of success falls or the costs escalate, but management may be reluctant to take the decision because of the optimism of the research staff, and the expenditure already incurred. In this event, the inclusion of the project in the selection process will aid the decision. More difficult, perhaps, is knowing when to finalise a project because of:

(a) The desire to be technically perfect
(b) Personal interests of the research workers.

SCHEDULING

The programme cannot be considered complete until the work has been scheduled. At the minimum, this will indicate when the appropriate staff are available and when they will finish their part of the programme. With the extension of network techniques such as PERT to multi-project scheduling, it is possible to schedule the work in detail and at the same time arrange an equitable work load. If this is done it can influence the programme, since a factor that can be quantified will be the optimum utilisation of resources.

During scheduling, it may be necessary to consider a cut-off decision on an existing project, to allow the inclusion of a new project with a higher ranking. It is generally considered that this should only be done if the existing project has a lower probability of success than the new project. A more accurate method would appear to be comparison of the expected achievement factors, taking into account the slope of this function for the existing project (see Chapter 8).

During this finalisation of the programme, the employment of consultants can be considered, especially if there are areas of work in which specialist knowledge is not available. Thought should also be given to whether the work could be done more profitably by a research association or university, for example, if they already have the necessary facilities.

APPROVAL

The final approval of the programme must be the responsibility of the Board, when it will be considered in conjunction with the budget. Availability of money will obviously be the determining factor. For private venture this may be limited to a percentage of the sales billed; in the case of a central laboratory of a large organisation, to what the product departments are willing to pay. If, however, the strategy is good, and in particular for breakthrough strategies, the imposition of a ceiling could be shortsighted.

In seeking Board approval, a *field of interest* statement[5] may be submitted. In this, the manufacturing groups are asked to describe their product areas in terms of function, rather than of manufactured goods; the function descriptions are made as broad as possible without overlapping the area of another division or extending beyond areas that can reasonably be covered by the technology and know-how of the division. A chart is then made showing the functional areas covered by each project. This may be backed by a *product market chart* which shows the current products, those being developed, and the types of customers to which they are sold or will be sold.

In some organisations the approval of the programme does not necessarily mean automatic approval of each project included in that programme; this applies particularly when the project will not commence until some time in the future, or is contingent on some factors, such as the receipt of a contract. Approval will then be sought at the appropriate time, when the budget, actual expenditure and status of the programme may be examined.

R & D Administration

REFERENCES

1. HERTZ, D. B., CARLSON, P. G., 'Selection, evaluation and control of research and development projects', *Conference on Applications of Operations Research to R & D Management*, Case Institute of Technology, Cleveland (1962)
2. MOTLEY, C. M., NEWTON, R. D., 'The selection of projects for industrial research', *15th Nat. Mtg. Operations Res. Soc. America*, Washington, DC (1959)
3. CHURCHMAN, C. W., ACKOFF, R. L., ARNOFF, E. L., Chapter 6, *Introduction to Operations Research*, John Wiley Inc., NY (1957)
4. MCWHORTER, W. F., 'A supervisory tool for evaluating design', *IEEE Trans. Engng. Mgmt.*, **EM-13**, No. 2, p. 91 (1966)
5. COLLIER, D. W., 'Programming research in a decentralised multidivisional company', *Res. Mgmt.*, **9**, No. 3, p. 161 (1966)

BIBLIOGRAPHY

SUITS, C. G., *Selectivity and Timing in Research*, Address, Industrial Research Institute, Colorado Springs, Colorado, May (1962)
KALGAR, D. W., MURDICK, R. G., *Managing Engineering and Research*, The Industrial Press, NY (1963)
MORANIAN, T., *The Research and Development Engineer as Manager*, Rutgers, The State University, Holt, Rinehart and Winston (1963)
PERLMAN, J., 'Measurements of scientific research and development and related activities', Chapter 2, *Operations Research in Research and Development*, Ed. Dean, B. V., John Wiley Inc., NY (1963)
HAWKINS, H. M., MARTIN, O. E., 'How to evaluate projects', *Chem. Engng. Progr.*, **60**, No. 12, p. 58 (1964)
POUND, W. H., 'Research projects selection; testing a model in the field', *IEEE Trans. Engng. Mgmt.*, **EM-11**, No. 1, p. 16 (1964)
Selectivity—A Modern Research Necessity, Address, American Management Association, Chicago, Illinois, Sept (1964). In *Speaking of Research*, John Wiley Inc., NY (1965)
BOEHM, J. E., 'Don't overlook competition', *Electron. Ind.*, **29**, No. 9, p. 127 (1965)
BULLARD, SIR E., 'What makes a good research establishment', in *The Organisation of Research Establishments*, Ed. Cockroft, Sir J., Cambridge University Press, (1965)
HART, A., 'Evaluation of R & D projects', *Chem. & Ind.*, No. 13, p. 549, (1965)
HEYMONT, I., *et al*, *Guide for Reviewers of Studies containing Cost-Effectiveness Analysis*, Research Analytic Corporation, Mclean, Virginia (1965)
MCNAIR, R. J., SHODLEY, F. C., 'Independent research planning and implementation', *IEEE Trans. Aerosp. Electron. Syst.*, **AES-1**, No. 2, p. 202 (1965)
SEILER, R. E., *Improving the Effectiveness of Research and Development*, McGraw-Hill Inc. (1965)
SIGFIRD, J. V., PARVIN, R. H., 'Project pattern; a methodology for determining relevance in complex decision making', *IEEE Trans. Engng. Mgmt.*, **EM-12**, No. 1, p. 9 (1965)
VAN TARSEL, K. R., 'Managing research and development', *Res. Mgmt.*, **8**, No. 9, p. 127 (1965)
HART, A., 'Chart for evaluating product research and development projects', *Operations Res. Quart.*, **17**, No. 4, p. 347 (1966)
KENDALL, W. S., 'Market research in the defence industry', *Electron. & Commun.*, p. 14, 7, 9, 11, May, July, September, November (1966)
'Selection of topics for research', Report on discussions held jointly by the *IEEE/IERE*, *Electron. & Power*, **12**, p. 12, 114, January, April (1966)

Chapter 6

Estimating and Price Fixing

The purpose of R & D in industry is to keep existing products competitive by improving them, to develop new products to replace or supplement them, and to explore new possibilities for expansion which will offer opportunity for making profits. This declaration of purpose also holds for the academic field if the term 'profits' is read as 'contributions to the sum of knowledge' and in the military field, if it is taken to mean 'gain in military power'. It is on this basis of cost effectiveness that projects are normally selected and reviewed, as discussed in Chapter 5. Furthermore, funds must be made available as required. For these purposes, it is necessary to prepare an *estimate* at the conception of a project, and to revise it continually during the life of the project. This chapter sets out a logical procedure for preparing an estimate and suggests a suitable routine for *price fixing*.

THE PLACE OF THE ESTIMATE

An estimate is a plan of work in terms of money. Hence, the work to be done must be defined before the plan and estimate can be derived. In many production jobs, the work can be defined rigidly by drawings and specifications, thereby enabling a definite plan to be formulated. The estimator can then predict the cost of the work to a high degree of accuracy. The other extreme is 'blue sky' pure research, where the work is defined so loosely that even the end result may be unknown. Consideration of the *decision processes* that must arise,[1] however, indicates that a plan of work can always be formulated and hence an estimate derived which will be contingent upon the unknown factors.

In any project there must be a logical progression of work from which the initial plan is derived. Referring to Fig. 6.1 for Phase 2 of a *development project*, the process will be:

(a) Defining the project
(b) Dividing the work into areas or *tasks*, which may be either

69

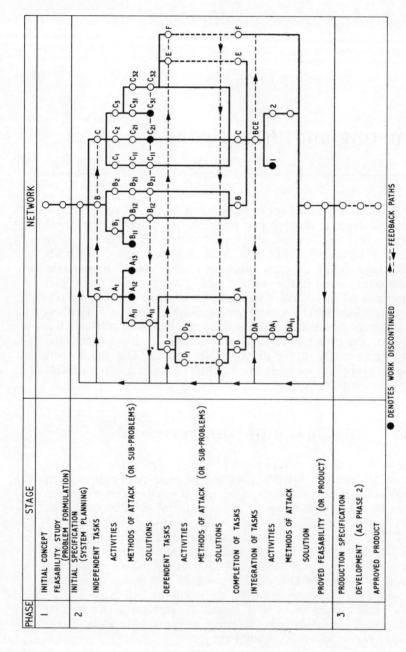

PHASE	STAGE	NETWORK
1	INITIAL CONCEPT	
	FEASABILITY STUDY (PROBLEM FORMULATION)	
2	INITIAL SPECIFICATION (SYSTEM PLANNING)	
	INDEPENDENT TASKS	
	ACTIVITIES	
	METHODS OF ATTACK (OR SUB-PROBLEMS)	
	SOLUTIONS	
	DEPENDENT TASKS	
	ACTIVITIES	
	METHODS OF ATTACK (OR SUB-PROBLEMS)	
	SOLUTIONS	
	COMPLETION OF TASKS	
	INTEGRATION OF TASKS	
	ACTIVITIES	
	METHODS OF ATTACK	
	SOLUTION	
	PROVED FEASABILITY (OR PRODUCT)	
3	PRODUCTION SPECIFICATION	
	DEVELOPMENT (AS PHASE 2)	
	APPROVED PRODUCT	

● DENOTES WORK DISCONTINUED   ----▸ FEEDBACK PATHS

Fig. 6.1. The development of an R & D project

independent or *dependent*, the latter being those that cannot be started or considered until another task reaches a certain stage

(c) Deciding all courses of action by which each task can be completed. This gives rise to the various problems and sub-problems, that is *activities*, that will have to be solved

(d) Selecting those courses of action by which the activities are most likely to be achieved

(e) Specifying the time limit (or limit of expenditure) for proving the feasibility of the courses of action (activities) selected. Alternative courses of action may be worked on in parallel or series

(f) Allocating priority to courses of action which are likely to give the best results not only technically, but also in terms of R & D and subsequent production costs

(g) Delaying any independent tasks that will be useless, if another task or tasks proves unfeasible

(h) Modifying (a), (b) and (c) according to the solutions obtained.

In the early stages of an ill-defined programme, the plan of work must allow for possible setbacks and changes, that is, *contingencies* must be allocated to those areas in which unknown tasks and/or activities may arise. Similarly, where feasibility is deemed to be low, provision must be made for investigating alternatives as well as continuing work for a prolonged period. As the project proceeds, there will be less need for risk margins and it will be possible to make a more accurate estimate; for this reason estimates must be reviewed continually.

It is essential that an estimate is always realistic, even in its appreciation of contingencies. *Over-expenditure* commits the management to further sums or losing the money already spent, and may result in a loss of confidence in the project. It is dangerous to guard against this by padding, since an excessive estimate may prove fatal to the project, particularly if it is the subject of a competitive tender; also, 'feather-bedding' often results in inefficient practices. Occasionally, *under-expenditure* may be forgiven, and even praised, but if this happens consistently it can prove embarrassing, and subsequent estimates may be trimmed severely.

INITIAL PLANNING AND ESTIMATING

The preparation of proposals and estimates for a project involves effort, and hence must be authorised by the R & D manager; this may be done by issuing a form similar to that shown in Fig. 8.3 (p. 120). This effort is usually charged to overheads, but subsequently may be transferred to the project if it is approved.

All research must start with certain proposals; even for pure research, a programme of work over some limited period can be envisaged. When an end objective is defined, the detail of the initial programming will be limited by the extent of this definition; to ensure that all aspects are considered, even if they cannot be specified, the use of a standard form is recommended. The format of such a *requirement specification* will naturally depend on the type of end product, but it may be no more than a check list, completed by reference to documents and standard specifications; an example from the telecommunication field is shown in Table 6.1.

For projects in which the end objective has been stated, the method of evolving the work plan as described in the previous section, has been formalised in the PERT system. The initial framework for assessing the work is obtained by making a *work breakdown structure*, an example of which is given in Fig. 6.2. This breakdown is product orientated and may be compared with an engineering parts list, in that the whole is broken down into assemblies, sub-assemblies, and parts. The breakdown should fall naturally into various *levels of indenture*, the lowest or *end item sub-divisions* being determined by the requirement specification; if the specification is indefinite, contingency end items may have to be

Table 6.1. A REQUIREMENT SPECIFICATION USED IN THE TELECOMMUNICATION FIELD*

Requirement Specification No.	
Short title	
General description	
Cost bracket; R & D	PRODUCTION
Required performance	Output power Modulation characteristics Input/output impedances Distortion Response Stability
Operational environment	Vibration/acceleration Climatic/temperature Radio interference
Supplies/services	Normal Standby
Physical characteristics	Size Weight Form factor
Associated and ancillary equipment	Aerial system Input/control units Test equipment
Life required	M.T.B.F.
Maintenance	Spares required Period for which spares must be available
Inspection standard	
Acceptance procedure	
Installation and commissioning procedures	
Packaging	
Other relevant information	

*Courtesy: Ultra Electronics Limited

72

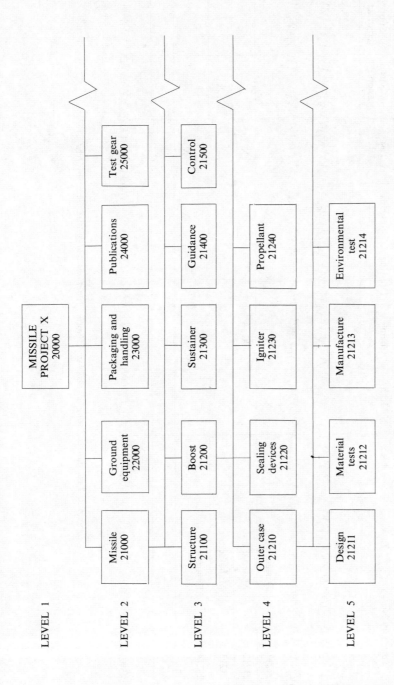

Fig. 6.2. Work breakdown structure showing levels of indenture. Courtesy: The Ministry of Technology

DESIGN DEPARTMENTS

Summary No.	Task	Elec.	Mech.	Chem.	Drawing office	Systems Eng.	Test lab.	Model shop.	Sub contract
21211	Design		X	X	X	X			
21212	Material tests			X		X	X		
21213	Manufacture		X		X			X	
21214	Environmental test					X	X		
21215									

Fig. 6.3. Task matrix listing all tasks and showing functions and/or disciplines involved

added. The end items will define the tasks to be accomplished. It must be remembered, however, that there are also tasks such as the integrations of end items into higher level items, programme management and systems engineering, which may not be product orientated, but which nevertheless should be included in the work breakdown structure.

To delineate the functions and/or disciplines involved in each task, a *task matrix* can be drawn as shown in Fig. 6.3. This ensures that relevant personnel are consulted at the time that the courses of action are being deliberated.

Each task will include one or more activities, and the major errors in estimating will arise due to:

(a) Inability to forecast all details of an activity
(b) Failure to identify all activities
(c) Changes to requirement specification, amending and/or adding activities.

By careful consideration of the problems, and by drawing on past experience, the project manager in consultation with his staff should be able to specify one or more courses of action by which each task should be accomplished, and the time required within certain limits.

To enable this to be done logically, a standard form such as that shown in Fig. 6.4 is recommended. The information needed for this form will also be required for scheduling the work and for ascertaining that the project will come within the approved budget. In addition, this form plays an important role in the subsequent control of the work, which is discussed in Chapter 8.

For each activity or sub-problem that can be foreseen, a form should be completed defining the area of work and the proposed course of action, and giving any other relevant information. The type and grade of effort, for example senior engineers, engineers, assistants, model shop, and drawing office, required in each period should be entered. The most convenient period, and that normally used with PERT, is the week, when the entries can be made in *man-weeks*. (With a five day week, half a day is 0·1 man-week and this is the limit of accuracy in assessing R & D.) For accountancy purposes *man-hours* are sometimes preferred, particularly for staff who may be paid overtime; (conversion is easily made from man-weeks.) The use of *man-months* is not recommended since the number of working days per month varies, and the effects of 'time-off' are not so apparent. If they are used, however, Table 6.2 will be of assistance; this gives the conversion to hours assuming a 40 hour week.

Allowance must be made for holidays, sickness, attending conferences and other extra-project activities. A typical allowance for an R & D laboratory is 25%, but company records should enable an exact figure to be obtained. This means that over a period, for a nominal 40 hour week, the average *effective hours* will be of the order of 30; this must be taken into account by increasing the weekly effort or extending the completion date.

PROJECT TITLE	
TASK	
ACTIVITY Starting Event / Finishing Event	
COURSE OF ACTION	

Week		1/27	2/28	3/29	4/30	5/31	6/32	7/33	8/34	9/35	10/36	11/37	12/38	1.
Date														
Senior Staff	E													
	A													
Staff	E													
	A													
Assist.	E													
	A													
D.O.	E													
	A													
Model Shop	E													
	A													
Expenses	E													
	A													
Consum. Mat.	E													
	A													
Sub-Contract	E													
	A													
In-feed	E													
	A													
Cap. Equip.	E													
	A													
Special Facilities	E													
	A													
Status	>													
	=													
	<													

COST ACCOUNTS REF.	PROJECT LEADER	PROJ. MANAGE

(a)

Fig. 6.4. Standard form to indicate courses of action, and time required

STIMATE & PROGRESS RECORD　　　　　E = Estimate　　A = Actual

R.S. No.

Event No.
Event No.

Sole/Alternative

4/40	15/41	16/42	17/43	18/44	19/45	20/46	21/47	22/48	23/49	24/50	25/51	26/52

PERT REF.	EST. START DATE	SHEET
		OF

ir completion. (a) Front of form; (b) Reverse of form (shown overleaf)

ACTIVITY/WORK PACKAGE

REMARKS

REQUIREMENTS—DETAILS	SUPPLIER

AMENDMENT	DATE	APPROVED	DATE

CUSTOMER ORDE

(b)

Fig. 6.4. continue

RELEVANT INFORMATION

RDER NO.	DATE	ACK.	DEL. REQD.	RECEIVED

REMARKS

LIAISON

Reverse of form

Table 6.2. MANPOWER CHART GIVING CONVERSION OF MAN-MONTHS TO HOURS ASSUMING A 40 HOUR WEEK*

STAFF vs. TIME

							NUMBER OF MEN								
	1/4	1/3	1/2	2/3	3/4	1	2	3	4	5	6	7	8	9	10
NUMBER OF MONTHS															
1/4	11	14	22	29	33	43	87	130	173	217	260	303	347	390	433
1/2	22	29	43	58	65	87	173	260	347	433	520	607	693	780	867
3/4	33	43	65	87	98	130	260	390	520	650	780	910	1040	1170	1300
1	43	58	87	116	130	173	347	520	693	867	1040	1213	1387	1560	1733
2	87	115	173	231	260	347	693	1040	1387	1733	2080	2427	2773	3120	3467
3	130	173	260	347	390	520	1040	1560	2080	2600	3120	3640	4160	4680	5200
4	173	231	347	462	520	693	1387	2080	2773	3467	4160	4853	5547	6240	6933
5	217	289	433	578	650	867	1733	2600	3467	4333	5200	6067	6933	7800	8667
6	260	346	520	694	780	1040	2080	3120	4160	5200	6240	7280	8320	9360	10400
7	303	404	607	809	910	1213	2427	3640	4853	6067	7280	8493	9707	10920	12133
8	347	462	693	925	1040	1387	2773	4160	5547	6933	8320	9707	11093	12480	13867
9	390	519	780	1040	1170	1560	3120	4680	6240	7800	9360	10920	12480	14040	15600
10	433	577	867	1156	1300	1733	3467	5200	6933	8667	10400	12133	13867	15600	17333
11	477	635	953	1272	1430	1907	3813	5720	7627	9533	11440	13347	15253	17160	19067
12	520	693	1040	1387	1560	2080	4160	6240	8320	10400	12480	14560	16640	18720	20800
WORKING DAYS per MONTH															
17	34	45	68	91	102	136	272	408	544	680	816	952	1088	1244	1360
18	36	48	72	96	108	144	288	432	576	720	864	1008	1152	1296	1440
19	38	51	76	101	114	152	304	456	608	760	912	1064	1216	1368	1520
20	40	53	80	107	120	160	320	480	640	800	960	1120	1280	1440	1600
21	42	56	84	112	126	168	336	504	672	840	1008	1176	1344	1512	1680
22	44	59	88	117	132	176	352	528	704	880	1056	1232	1408	1584	1760
23	46	61	92	123	138	184	368	552	736	920	1104	1288	1472	1656	1840
24	48	64	96	128	144	192	384	576	768	960	1152	1344	1536	1728	1920
25	50	67	100	133	150	200	400	600	800	1000	1200	1400	1600	1800	2000
26	52	69	104	139	156	208	416	624	832	1040	1248	1456	1664	1872	2080
27	54	72	108	144	162	216	432	648	864	1080	1296	1512	1728	1944	2160
28	56	75	112	149	168	224	448	672	896	1120	1344	1568	1792	2016	2240
29	58	77	116	155	174	232	464	696	928	1160	1392	1624	1856	2088	2320
30	60	80	120	160	180	240	480	720	960	1200	1440	1680	1920	2160	2400
31	62	83	124	165	186	248	496	744	992	1240	1488	1736	1984	2232	2480

*Reproduced with acknowledgement to Electronic Industries.

The *effort loading* will extend from the start of the activity to the 'most likely' finishing period. If the activity is one of a number of alternatives, the period at which significant results may be expected should be marked (the cut-off date); this date can also be useful as a milestone for control purposes.

Where *network analysis techniques* (see Chapter 7) are used, an *optimistic* period must be marked. This is defined as the earliest possible date by which the activity could be completed provided that no unforeseen problems arise. The effort may be extended to a *pessimistic* date, that is, the date by which, assuming there is no cut-off despite the worst eventualities, the activity is bound to be finished.

Under normal circumstances the effort loading is dictated by the number of staff expected to be available. When the finishing date is specified, however, this should be treated as the pessimistic date; the effort per period needed to meet this date must be stated precisely, after which the other dates can be marked. In such circumstances it will be management responsibility to provide the extra effort or to authorise some compromise in the programme.

Other costs arising directly from the activity should be entered on the form in the periods for which they will be required or committed. Any special equipment or facilities must also be stated precisely. (These costs are discussed further in the next section.)

With the initial activity completed, a starting date can be given for the ensuing dependent activity; the process is repeated until each task, and finally the project, is completed. When any activity is one of a number of alternatives, then if the activities are worked in series, the completion date should be taken as the completion date of one, plus the cut-off periods of all the others.

It is essential for these forms to be completed in consultation with the staff who will do the work when the project is authorised, since research workers in general tend to avoid giving estimates, particularly when predictability is low. To ensure consultation and the careful examination of the problems, the forms should be completed and signed by the project engineer, who should be free to record any reservations or recommendations. This procedure also tends to correct over-optimism on the part of the project manager; furthermore, when the work is under way, the project engineer will exert pressure on himself to try and keep to his promised dates.

PRICE FIXING

The summarising and conversion into terms of money of the basic estimates must follow accepted accountancy practices in the *allocation of the costs*. The estimator must, therefore, be cognisant of the terms used, and the procedure to be followed in determining the *final price*. This has been summarised in Table 6.3[2], but the practice in a particular company may vary in detail. Because of this the use of an *allocation sheet* is

Table 6.3. SUMMARY OF TYPICAL PROJECT AND/OR PRODUCT COSTS

1. Prime Costs
   (a) Direct material
       (material used entirely on job)
       1. Raw material
       2. Bought-out items
       3. Sub-contracted items
          (Allowances may be made for scrap, wastage and redundant items)

   (b) Direct labour
       (labour used entirely on the job)
       1. Professional scientific and engineering effort
       2. Experimental labour
       3. Drawing office
       4. Model shop
       5. Production labour

   (c) Direct expenses
       (expenses incurred solely and entirely because of the job)
       1. Special equipment
       2. Special facilities
       3. Travelling expenses for project conferences, trials, etc.

2. Overheads
   (a) Direct
       (production or laboratory)
       1. Rent, rates, taxes and insurance of premises accommodating the work
       2. Fuel, gas, water, lighting, heat and cleaning of above premises
       3. Patent fees, and royalties (in some cases these may be a direct expense)
       4. Administrative salaries (usually up to and including the manager)
       5. Repairs, renewals, depreciation of plant, equipment, buildings, etc.
       6. Supporting facilities, e.g. inspection, test, library
       7. Overtime, premiums, holidays, sick pay, etc.

   (b) Indirect (office)
       1. Rent, rates, taxes and insurance of offices
       2. Lighting, heating, cleaning, etc., of offices
       3. Salaries of directors, office staff, representatives (liaison engineers)
       4. Depreciation of office equipment
       5. General expenses, e.g., advertising, transport
       6. Stationery, postage, etc.

3. The Factory or Works Cost   = Prime cost plus direct overheads

4. Total Cost   = Works cost plus indirect overheads

5. Selling Price   = Total cost plus profit

recommended to ensure consistency. A typical example is the one required from contractors by United Kingdom Government Ministries, detailing which charges are direct and which are indirect. Such a sheet will be completed by the accountant in consultation with the manager; any departure from the policy expressed in it should only be made in exceptional circumstances, with the approval of all parties. On page 81 it was stressed that the basic estimate should specify 'all requirements'; this will show if a project makes an unduly heavy call on some effort or facility which is normally an indirect charge. In such an event the true *cost recovery* might not be made and it will be subsidised by other projects. Such exceptional circumstances may also occur when a senior staff member, whose salary is included normally in overheads, is expected to spend an appreciable part of his time on the project.

The expected direct labour cost will be obtained by multiplying the expected effort by a *costing rate*, which will be given by the accounts department. A separate costing rate may be given for each grade of effort delineated, for each year over which the project extends, but this is not always done.

The costing rate is normally the arithmetic average of all salaries in the grade, or grades, less that part chargeable to overheads, expressed as a rate per hour, week, month, or year. The part chargeable to overheads, including holidays, sickness pay, is shown in Table 6.3. This costing rate is not the rate that will be actually booked to the job, as can be seen from the following example:

If 40 man-weeks have been estimated for a job, then assuming allowances of 25%, the time asked will be $(40 \times 100/75)$ man-weeks. If the annual salary is £1,500, then the weekly salary less that portion charged to overheads, that is the weekly costing rate, is $£(1500/52 \times 75/100)$; and the estimated cost (£) will be:

$$\left(40 \times \frac{100}{75}\right) \times \left(\frac{1500}{52} \times \frac{75}{100}\right) = 40 \times \frac{1500}{52}$$

which is the estimated time multiplied by the actual weekly rate.

It appears from this that making the allowances is an unnecessary complication; but only by so doing can a reasonable time and effort estimate be prepared, for checking with the budgets and providing a correct foundation for planning. Moreover, the nature of R & D estimating is such that the estimator may include automatically the allowances in his figures, particularly when he is considering an extended period; in this case if the actual rate was applied, the cost would be over-estimated.

The basic estimates will include sums for the purchase of materials, piece parts and components which are necessary to complete the work, but which will have no residual value. Such materials are termed *consumable* and this value should be entered on the estimate at the expected time of commitment. This procedure should be fairly straightforward for items of comparatively large monetary value, while for minor items, past records should indicate a suitable sum per research worker per

83

period, together with the pattern of expenditure. When consumable supplies are not of great monetary value, or when they are shared by many projects, for example, chemicals, it may be convenient to include them under overheads as services. It will be found desirable, and for United Kingdom Government contracts it is necessary, to separate *in-feed items*, that is items purchased from other divisions of the company, since such costs should not include profit. Any special tooling or test equipment required for development may be considered consumable, but should be shown separately as they may have a transfer value, that is, a nominal value for transference to another contract.

If any of the R & D work is sub-contracted either to an outside organisation or to a separate division of the company, the costs should be shown separately and should be supported by estimates or quotations.

When personnel engaged on the project are likely to incur travelling expenses, these expenses should be included in the basic estimate, together with the expected period of commitment. Travelling expenses for other staff are normally included in overheads and can be omitted from the estimate; if they are expected to be exceptionally large, however, special action can be considered for their recovery.

In addition to consumable material there may be requirements for *capital* equipment. This is defined as equipment which will have a definite residual value at the end of the project. As such, if it is purchased by the company it becomes part of the company's fixed assets, the initial cost being charged to the capital account and not the project, whilst depreciation and maintenance will be provided for in the overheads. However, special equipment that is required for a specific project and is unlikely to be used after completion of the project may be charged to direct expenses and the residual value, if any, will be credited to direct expenses. When the R & D work is being done on behalf of a customer, it is preferable for the customer to pay for such equipment, which becomes his own property; but he cannot be expected to pay for equipment that the company would be expected to have in the normal course of its business, for example, oscilloscopes and voltmeters.

In addition to capital equipment, the provision of special facilities may include special *layouts*. This can comprise changes to the laboratory layout, new partitions, extensions, provision of extra supplies, etc. Although the project engineer may request these in his basic estimate, it is not in his province to provide an estimate, and this must be done by the appropriate specialist. The cost of such changes is included normally in overheads, when it is the accountant's responsibility to ensure that the overhead rate ensures recovery. As with capital equipment, if such costs are abnormal and are only required for a specific project, special consideration may be given to making them a direct charge.

In some circumstances, *duty* and/or *royalty* may have to be paid on components or equipment either imported or made under licence. Any such sums should be distinguished, since either they form an item of direct-cost, or they may be mitigated by regulations in the United Kingdom and the United States for Government contracts.

The project manager will follow the accountant's instructions regarding *overheads*, the main methods of allocation being:

(a) *Machine rate.* An hourly charge for the use of a specific machine or machines. This could be appropriate for work, for example with a nuclear reactor or computer, where the running cost of the machine is the major charge. This may be combined with a labour rate as given in (b) and (c) below.

(b) *Hourly burden.* The total expenses, that is, all wages and overheads, divided by the number of hours worked is termed the hourly burden. This gives a flat rate per hour, and is probably the most popular system in R & D organisations. To take into account the varying grades of labour that may be used, wage and overhead rates can be calculated separately.

(c) *Percentage on wages.* This is more applicable to production work, since it necessitates fixing a wage rate for each class of labour and expressing the overheads as a percentage of this wage rate.

(d) *Material rate.* This is a percentage on direct material costs, and is usually taken in conjunction with a labour rate. It is only used if material costs are high in relation to labour costs, or where there is an abnormal amount of material handling and storage.

When indirect overheads are separated from direct overheads, they are usually expressed as a 'percentage on the work cost'.

Knowing which charges are direct and which are indirect, the project leader can summarise the activity estimates. A form used for the evaluation of the *total cost* is shown in Fig. 6.5. (This form meets a number of other requirements which are discussed later.) If, in transferring the activity totals, the project leader considers the research worker has been optimistic, he should extend the totals without informing him or altering the activity estimate, but should give his reasons on the summary. The project leader should also include any items that are normally indirect, but which he considers should in this instance be made direct; such items should be marked specially, for example by ringing, and the reasons for their inclusion as a direct charge given on the form; they should not, however, be included in the totals until approved. Summaries of capital equipment and special facilities can be given on the reverse of this form (Fig. 6.5(b)).

These summaries can now be submitted to the R & D manager for approval and to initiate any special action that might be required, such as the transference of indirect costs to direct; if he considers the project leader has been optimistic he may either return the summaries for revision or, without informing the project leader, may recommend a *contingency* when the estimate is passed for authorisation. Such a contingency may be based solely on personal knowledge of the project leader, without reference to the project.

During the preparation of the estimate, the project leader will have been advised by the R & D manager of the resources available for the project within the overall budget for the laboratory, the allocation of

85

Note: If costs are not derived directly
from activity estimate, identify and
detail changes on reverse.   ESTIMATE

Task No.	Activity No.	Description and Remarks	Cost Heading	Actual Costs Committed	Quarter
		Total			
		Total			
		Total			
		Total			
		Total			
		Grand Totals			

RS No.	Project	Customer

(a)

Fig. 6.5. Standard form for estimated project cost

OJECT COSTS (direct labour, materials and overheads) Issue No.
Revised

				Estimates				
Quarter	Quarter	Quarter	Half Year	Half Year	Year	Year	Year	Total
					Project No.		Sheet No.	
							Of	

) Front of form; (b) Reverse of form (shown overleaf)

RATES

Cost Heading	Year												
	Rate	O/H	Total	Rate	O/H	Total	Rate	O/H	Total	Rate	O/H	Total	

CAPITAL EQUIPMENT

Description	Cost	Date Required	Sanction		
			Applied	Ref.	Granted
Total					

SPECIAL FACILITIES

Description	Cost	Date Required	Sanction		
			Applied	Ref.	Granted
Total					

EXCESSIVE EXPENDITURE IN O/H ALLOCATION

Description	Cost	O/H Allocation	Period	Action

ACTIVITY ESTIMATE—RESERVE CONTINGENCY ADDED

Activity	Week and Date / Cost Heading											

ISSUE NO. AND DATE

No.		
Date		
Signed		

Fig. 6.5. (continued), (b) Reverse of form

(b)

which was discussed in Chapter 4. The format of the summaries has therefore been designed to conform to that of the budget forecasts, which are prepared on the basis of:

(a) A manpower budget
(b) A financial budget for material, labour, and overhead expenditure
(c) A capital budget.

This will help the R & D manager to ensure that the project fits within the framework of the budget, otherwise the objectives will have to be lowered or additional resources appropriated. In extreme cases the project might have to be deferred or dropped.

In certain circumstances the scheduling of the project, which is dealt with in Chapter 7, may affect the total cost; this is another aspect that may have to be investigated by the R & D manager.

It is highly probable that delays, difficulties and unforeseen activities will arise during development. The main causes of these are:

(a) The magnitude of the technological advance entailed
(b) The length of the development period
(c) What has been achieved in the development programme at the time of the estimate
(d) The estimator and/or contractor.

To cover these eventualities, a sum of money termed a *contingency* or *risk margin* over and above the total cost estimated must be made available, to draw on as and when required. The amount of this margin, which may be given as a percentage of the works cost or total cost, is normally a guess on the part of the manager based on past experience; attempts are now being made by some companies to codify this practice by making a statistical analysis of the errors that have occurred in past projects. This technique has been termed *de-biasing*.

It is possible for the manager to submit an estimate based on the pessimistic periods of completion, which were required on the basic estimate for each task activity; but it is unlikely that everything will go wrong and in consequence the pessimistic cost will not be realistic. A better method is that based on a *costs on* PERT (COP) technique. This involves the preparation of estimate summaries for the optimistic and pessimistic periods, as well as for the most likely. From the three resulting works costs, and assuming, as with PERT, that the probability of expenditure has a beta distribution, a formula can be derived for the *most probable cost*. This is defined statistically as having a probability of 50%; that is, if the estimate has been prepared properly there are equal chances that the final cost will be either below or above this figure.

The most probable cost is equal to:

$$\frac{(\text{optimistic cost}) + (4 \times \text{most likely cost}) + (\text{pessimistic cost})}{6}$$

and the standard deviation $= \dfrac{(\text{pessimistic cost}) - (\text{optimistic cost})}{6}$

If the most probable cost is quoted, the risk margin can be defined in terms of the standard deviation (σ) according to the usual probability definitions, as follows:

(a) 1 in 4   chance that cost will be exceeded, add $0 \cdot 6745\sigma$
(b) 1 in 6   ,,   ,,   ,,   ,,   ,,   ,,   ,, σ
(c) 1 in 364   ,,   ,,   ,,   ,,   ,,   ,,   ,, 2σ
(d) 1 in 7400   ,,   ,,   ,,   ,,   ,,   ,,   ,, 3σ

In addition to the contingency required because of events that may arise during development within the laboratory, the manager may consider that a supplier of parts or facilities, who may be the customer, is optimistic in his prices or time scale; if this occurs he should recommend a *general contingency*. Such a contingency should be kept confidential between the management and customer, since in most cases the money will not be allocated until the events arise and it is proved to be necessary.

The total period over which the project will extend is often required concurrently with the estimate. This can only be assessed with reasonable accuracy by detailed planning techniques such as those described in Chapter 7. If, however, the estimates have been prepared as described above, they will indicate a most likely finishing date, to which can be added the risk margin converted back into periods of a known effort level. The periods represented by the most probable cost and standard deviation can be determined in a similar way.

COST ESTIMATING RELATIONSHIPS

An experienced manager can often produce an accurate assessment of the cost of a new project from his knowledge of the broad problems involved, and by making adjustments for the risk that will arise on the basis of typical past performance of similar laboratory work. The acceptance of such an assessment by the Board can only be due to the manager having proved himself right in the past. In consequence attempts have been and are being made to give such 'broad brush' estimates a firmer basis, for example, by the use of the *parametric* and *life cycle* techniques in which a statistically derived formula gives the gross cost from a number of parameters.

In principle the parametric technique is not new, since the simplest example, that of estimating transformer costs from the weight of wire to be incorporated, has been known and used for many years.

Parametric equations are usually derived from computer analysis of similar past projects, using regression techniques and hence have the general form:

$$y = \sum_{1}^{n=m} \alpha_n x_n^{\theta_n}$$

where y = cost
          x_n = dependent variable, which may be either a single parameter, or a combination of parameters
        α_n, θ_n = empirical constants

91

Such equations need not be correct dimensionally, as can be seen from the examples given in Table 6.4. In examples **(B)** and **(C)** only one variable appears. This does not necessarily affect the accuracy of the formulae, however, since the fewer the number of independent variables, the greater is the number of statistical degrees of freedom; this increases the reliability of the regression. In a programme to develop C.E.R.

Table 6.4. COST ESTIMATING RELATIONSHIPS—EXAMPLES OF PARAMETRIC DERIVED FORMULAE

(A) Total development cost automatic flight control system[3]

$$C = 10^3 \left(-31 - 94\frac{MA}{10^4(Y-1950)} + 151\frac{W}{(Y-1950)} + 33f \right)$$

where C = total development cost in dollars
M = aircraft maximum mach number
A = maximum altitude in thousands of feet
Y = calendar year of programme start
W = weight of electronic units in pounds
f = complexity factor

(B) Procurement cost of military radio communications equipment[4]

$$C = 100 \ W^{0.7}$$

where W is for:

1. portable sets	19 P	
2. fixed, transportable sets	60 $P^{0.37}$	
3. shipborne sets	15 $P^{0.75}$	
4. vehicular sets	55 $P^{0.32}$	
5. airborne sets	19 $P^{0.43}$	

and P = power output in watts

(C) Acquisition cost of electronic data processing equipment[5]

1. acquisition cost of core storage	$C = 1734 \ S^{0.873}$
2. cost of magnetic tape handling unit	$C = 9664 \ t^{0.321}$
3. rental cost of magnetic tape handling unit	$C = 276 \ t^{0.252}$

where C = cost in dollars
S = storage capacity of memory unit (binary digits/1,000)
t = transfer rate in characters per second divided by 1,000

techniques, therefore, it may be more advantageous to analyse sub-systems or phases of work, for example reliability, prototype production, rather than complete projects or systems.

The life cycle technique[6] is defined as 'a model describing the way in which people work'. It takes as a premise that the amount of work which a group accomplishes in any given period depends on how long they have been working and the amount of work remaining; thus by interpreting a project's past history and current status, its future may be forecast. In theory, this technique is not dependent on the end item being developed, and the only information required is:

(a) For any one cycle, the months required to reach peak manpower in that cycle
(b) For the same cycle, the amount of manpower to be used at the peak of the cycle
(c) Factors which give relationships between successive cycles.

By defining, for any one project, one or more base cycles which can overlap or even form part of each other, but which can be estimated fairly readily, this technique enables the other defined cycles to be determined. This approach can also be used to revise the total estimate, as the costs of the base cycle become more accurately known, and to determine the budgetary costs over a period. Table 6.5 gives some relationships, based on the formula developed by Norden which have been used successfully by International Business Machines, but which may be unique to their programmes.

Confidence in C.E.R. methods will naturally depend on knowledge of how the formulae have been derived, and how accurate they prove to be in subsequent forecasting; but they must be applied with extreme care to programmes requiring some aspect of special research or development.

Table 6.5. COST ESTIMATING RELATIONSHIPS—EXAMPLE OF THE 'LIFE CYCLE' METHOD[7]

Let a = a coefficient which determines the month of peak manpower
H_E = number of man-months in any given month
H_{EC} = cumulative number of man-months to date for one cycle
H_{ET} = total number of man-months to complete one cycle
T = total cycle time
t = time in months from start of cycle
t_1 = month, within cycle, of maximum manpower usage
t_2 = month, within cycle, of curve inflexion in decrease of utilised manpower.

Then for any one cycle:

$$H_E = 2H_{ET} a T \exp(-at^2)$$
$$t_1 = \sqrt{\frac{1}{2a}}$$
$$t_2 = \sqrt{\frac{3}{2a}}$$
$$H_{ET} = 1 \cdot 65 (H_E)_{max} \, t_1$$
$$H_{EC} = H_{ET}(1 - \exp(at^2))$$
$$T = 3t_1$$

and the average relationship between cycles is:

Cycle	H_{ET}	T
Planning: design	4·0	1·4
Design: prototype	1·0	1·0
Prototype: release	1·0	1·0
Release: product support	0·4	0·7

It is not surprising that companies using these techniques have derived their own formulae from their actual costs on past projects, and that such companies are mostly engaged in the aerospace field, where development costs and risk factors are high, so that every means must be taken to check estimates.

COST RECOVERY

It is not out of place in this chapter to give consideration to the recovery of costs, since this may affect the final quoted price. When the risk margin is large or difficult to assess, as in pure R & D, the preferred method of recovery is *cost plus*; by this method, the company is enabled to recover the actual costs incurred together with profit at an agreed specified rate. A *limit of expenditure* is usually imposed, based on the estimated costs, and this is reviewed periodically in the light of results achieved and revised estimates to completion. When the financing is *private*, that is, the company or organisation is itself providing the funds, this is the only feasible method.

A customer may on occasion demand a *fixed price*. This can involve the company in a considerable risk, by having to complete the work regardless of cost, whilst the price to be received remains unchanged. This type of contract, therefore, can only be considered when the work has been defined fully and precisely by specifications which will remain unaltered. In such circumstances extra care must be taken in the preparation of the estimate, and the quoted price may be based on:

(a) Pessimistic cost, so that the firm bears no risk
(b) Pessimistic cost less the profit margin that will be added, subsequently, so that in the worst possible case the company will neither benefit nor lose
(c) Most likely cost plus arbitrary risk margin
(d) Most probable cost, plus multiple of standard deviation
(e) Political price. If there is foreknowledge of the price the customer is willing to pay, and the company is prepared to accept the risk, a low price, even that based on the optimistic estimate, might be quoted. Sometimes this is done in the hope that requirements will be changed during the contract, when the political price can be withdrawn, and a new realistic price quoted. This practice, which must be deprecated, is undoubtedly a cause of the escalation of R & D costs.

There are a number of compromises between cost plus and fixed price contracts, the chief being:

(a) *Cost plus fixed fee*. Instead of the profit being a percentage on cost, a fixed fee is negotiated. This gives the company an incentive to keep the costs low, in order to maximise profit on turnover
(b) *Incentive plan*. As costs increase over and above a certain figure

the profit percentage decreases until at a certain ceiling price no profit is allowed, or it may be related to performance, time, and cost goals[8,9]

(c) *Price to be agreed.* This starts as a cost plus contract, and continues until both parties consider there is sufficient information on which to agree a fixed price

(d) *Part cost.* Circumstances may arise in which the company and a customer will share the cost of a project. Such contracts are rare since they can give rise to both commercial and accounting difficulties.

It must be remembered that in all cases where an outside customer is involved there must be *provisional contract* cover, the correctness of which can only be determined by a good estimate.

UNITED STATES FEDERAL AGENCY CONTRACTS

The present policy of the Federal Government is that where a fixed price contract cannot be placed, an incentive contract rather than a cost plus should be awarded if at all possible. The concept of performance, time and cost goals is based on a critical appraisal of the PERT/TIME and PERT/COST information supplied initially by the contractor. (These are also planning and control procedures, and are discussed in detail in the next two chapters.)

The estimating principles discussed in this chapter supply the basic information required, but the detailed analysis arising from the PERT procedure will result in greater accuracy in forecasting the final price and time. There is the disadvantage, however, that such a detailed presentation can take a considerable time to prepare; in consequence, study contracts are often awarded to two or more contractors for a limited period in order that they may prepare their plan and carry out feasibility studies. When such studies are not awarded, the successful contractor may be permitted to charge the costs involved against the contract.

The negotiating procedure may be summarised[10] as follows:

(a) Reaffirm or revise technical specifications, time and cost reporting requirements

(b) Reach complete agreement on programme breakdown and level of reporting

(c) Assure that the contractor's breakdown, below the reporting level, is generating reliable data, and being processed in a manner to produce understandable, meaningful and dependable information for presentation to top level management

(d) Award contract and stipulate that the PERT/COST system be implemented and operated in accordance with the contractual work statement.

DEVELOPMENT COST PLAN

In the United Kingdom, it is a growing practice for Government Ministries to place an R & D contract in accordance with an approved *development cost plan* (D.C.P.). This is defined as 'a contractor's detailed cost programme to completion of the work entailed on a research and development project, appropriately analysed into areas of effort, milestones of expected achievement within these areas, and related estimates of cost, in such a form that during the course of the project, progress and costs to a given date can be compared with the original estimates to that date'.

Guidance to the preparation and presentation of the D.C.P., which can vary between Government Departments, is given by the Technical Director responsible for approval, after due discussion and assessment. In general the following points apply:

(a) The D.C.P. will cover the contractor's whole programme of work on a project, even though the Ministry may place separate contracts with the contractor for individual parts of that programme. In this event each contract must be identified separately.

(b) If the contractor has more than one factory, the D.C.P. should show in which factory each item of work is to be done

(c) Assumptions made in areas where it is not possible to give an accurate estimate (for example, where the programme is not defined clearly, or where difficulties are likely to occur), should be indicated. In appropriate cases alternative assumptions should be costed.

(d) Details of sub-contracts against each area of work should be given

(e) Items specifically included, or excluded, from the D.C.P. (such as significant items to be purchased, or items assumed to be embodiment loan) should be identified

(f) Additional capital facilities required, and their cost, should be detailed

(g) The estimated unit costs, related to the D.C.P. estimates, of the main items of hardware, (e.g. missile control system, guidance system) should be stated. Separate costs for R & D and acceptance are required. In addition, special test equipment, packaging, and technical publications should be identified separately

(h) The D.C.P. will be less profit, which will be added subsequently, and agreed wages and overhead rates will be used

(i) The contractor must make allowances within each area of work for the sort of delays and difficulties which experience shows are likely to occur, and should indicate in his comment the extent to which he has made such provision. He should not add a general unallocated contingency for unforseeable delays and difficulties not reflected in the programme. The Technical Director may, however, call for a general contingency from the Managing Director or Chief Executive of the contractor; such a contingency will not appear in the D.C.P. and will be confidential.

From the above, it will be seen that all the information required for the preparation of the estimate in the D.C.P. will be available if the procedure described previously has been followed. It may be noted that the format of the official form is similar to that shown in Fig. 6.5. In addition to the estimate, a plan of work is also required and this will be discussed in Chapter 7.

An important function of the D.C.P. is to provide a measure of Ministry control in a cost plus contract. This is achieved by the contractor furnishing a monthly return of expenditure, a quarterly return of costs, which also calls for the latest estimate, together with progress reports at regular intervals. A revised D.C.P. is also called for annually or if a major change in cost is envisaged. This control procedure is discussed in detail in Chapter 8.

REFERENCES

1. MARPLES, D. L., 'The decisions of engineering design', *Engng. Designer,* Dec. (1960)
2. GARBUTT, D., *Advanced Accounts, Carter's,* 5th edit., Pitman (1962)
3. *Technical Report ASD-TDR-62-751,* Air Force Systems Command, USA Oct. (1962)
4. REINHART, E. E., *Military Radio Communications Equipment Trade-Offs,* Electronics Dept., RAND Corporation Report P-1724, June (1959)
5. *Memos. on C.E.R. programme,* Air Force Systems Command, Aug., Sept. (1962)
6. NORDEN, P. V., 'On the anatomy of development projects', *IRE Trans. Engng. Mgmt.,* **EM-7**, No. 1, p. 34 (1960)
7. O'REILLY, F. J., *How to Make a Life-Cycle Analysis,* Development Laboratories, Data Systems Division, I.B.M. Corporation, Sept. (1961)
8. *Incentive Contracting,* Seminar, National Defence Education Institute, prepared by Harbridge House Inc. (1962)
9. *Armed Services Procurement Regulation,* Revision 2 Par. 3-808, Profit Aug. (1963)
10. MOODY, F. T., *An Introduction to PERT/COST,* Technical Report No. ESD-TDR-64-208, Techniques Branch, Electronics Systems Division, U.S. Air Department, March (1964)

BIBLIOGRAPHY

BUSH, G. P., HATTERY, L. H., (Eds.), *Scientific Research, its Administration and Organisation,* American University Press (1950)
Proc. Ann. Conf. Ind. Res., Columbia University, USA (1952)
The Direction of Research Establishments, Symposium, National Physical Laboratory, 1956, H.M.S.O. (1957)
Report of the Committee on the Management and Control of Research and Development, Office of the Minister for Science, H.M.S.O. (1961)
SOUTHALL, H. P., *The Management Accountant's Influence on Research and Development,* Institute of Cost and Works Accountants, Summer School (1961)
Development Cost Estimating Survey, Department of Defence, Washington, prepared by Management Systems Corporation, June (1963)
MORANIAN, T., *The Research and Development Engineer as Manager,* Rutgers, The State University, Holt, Rinehart and Winston (1963)
TRUEGER, P. M., *Accounting Guide for Defence Contracts,* Commerce Clearing House, NY, 4th edit. (1963)
ALLAN, T. J., 'Studies of the problem solving process in engineering design', *IEEE Trans. Engng. Mgmt.,* **EM-13**, No. 2, p. 72 (1966)

Chapter 7

Planning and Scheduling

Planning is in effect a simulation study of what may occur under certain conditions; it is a necessary aid for decision making.

(The continuing problems of time slippage and increase in cost of R & D programmes, both military and civil,[1, 2] due to unexpected technical difficulties, proved the ineffectiveness of planning systems in common use until about 1960. In 1958, PERT (Program Evaluation and Review Technique) was introduced and has since been developed to show the interdependence of *performance, time,* and *cost variables*. Its application has been successful in that it forces a depth of planning, allows for areas of uncertainty and has some predictive attributes. Because of this, the use of PERT is now called for in all major Government contracts, both in the United States and the United Kingdom.

It is conceded generally that PERT can be operated manually where there are fewer than one hundred activities; beyond that stage, a computer is necessary.

THE PERT NETWORK

The breakdown of a project into tasks and activities for the purpose of estimating costs was described in Chapter 6. This process is assisted by drawing the decision tree forecasting the problems (activities) and showing the sequence in which they may arise; this is, in effect, a planning *network*, but the format of the topology must be systematised to make the presentation meaningful.

The PERT network (see Fig. 7.1 and Fig. 7.2) is composed of *events* and *activities*. An event is a recognisable control point such as a specific accomplishment which consumes no time or resources, whilst an activity is, as defined previously, a job of work to be performed in association with an authority. On the network, an event is depicted by a circle, ellipse, or square, numbered in accordance with a master list; an activity is shown by an arrow connecting two events, termed the *predecessor (precursor)* and *successor* events, the numbers of which identify the activity.

The initial step in forming the network must be to establish its configuration. This is best done by considering each task and listing the events that must occur; the start can be any convenient point, which is sometimes determined after making a preliminary listing, and then working backwards or forwards. The networks for each task are then integrated into a complete network, which is 'event orientated'. But as the objective is to probe areas of uncertainty and establish the means by which an event can be achieved, the final configuration must be activity orientated. In the case of an extended programme, a compromise may

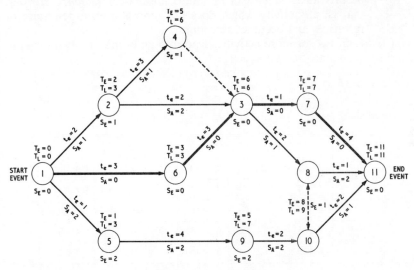

Fig. 7.1. A PERT *network*

$T_E = $ *Maximum value of sum of* t_e *from start to event*
$T_L = $ *Minimum value of* T_E *for end event less sum of* t_e *from end to event*
$S_E = T_L - T_E$
$S_A = T_L$ *(successor)* $-[T_E$ *(predecessor)* $+ t_e]$

be made by maintaining the network in detail, that is, specifying activities, for a period of about six months ahead, but listing only events beyond this period.

In establishing the network, the analyst must make sure that there is an event for:

(a) Each deliverable item, or milestone
(b) Each interface, that is, an event connecting with another point of the network, or with another network
(c) Each *check point*, that is, a point where a management decision has to be made. This is particularly relevent in a *feasibility* investigation, or when there are areas of uncertainty, when the check point may involve a cut-off decision. (In such circumstances there may be a series of networks each ending in a check point)

(d) The start and finish of every activity, that is, every activity has a predecessor and successor event.

There are also certain basic rules for the topology of the network:

(a) Every activity must have a predecessor and successor event
(b) No activity can start until its predecessor event has been completed, that is, all activities leading into that event are completed
(c) When two or more activities occur in parallel between the same predecessor and successor events, unique successor events should be provided, which can be interconnected by *dummy activities*, that is, an activity which does not represent an expenditure of resources and occupies zero time
(d) When two or more activities lead into an event, and two or more

(a)
ACTIVITIES

1	2		3	4	5	6	7	8	9	10	11	12	13
Description	Event		t_a	t_m	t_b	t_e	$(T_E)_s$	$(T_L)_p$	S_A	σ	σ^2	$(\sigma_E^2)_s$	$(\sigma_L^2)_p$
	P	S											
	1	2	1	2	3	2	2	1	1	0·3	0·1̄		
	2	3	1	1½	5	2	4	4	2	0·6̄	0·4̄		
	2	4	2	3	4	3	5	③	1	0·3	0·1̄		
	4	3	—	—	—	0	5	6	—	—	—		
	1	6	1	4	5	3	3	⓪	0	0·6̄	0·4̄	0·4	
	6	3	1	2	9	3	⑥	3	0	1·3̄	1·7̄	2·1	
	1	5	—	1	—	1	1	2	2	—	—		

(b)
EVENTS

Event		T_E	T_L	S_E	Slack Analysis							
Description	No.				0	1	2	3	4	5	6	7
	1	0	0	0	X							
	2	2	3	1		X						
	3	6	6	0	X							
	4	5	6	1		X						
	5	1	3	2			X					

Fig. 7.2. PERT/TIME—examples of forms for manual calculation. Note, Fig. 7.2(a):
1. Column 7—circle largest value of T_E when successor event appears more than once
2. Column 8—circle smallest value of T_L when predecessor event appears more than once
3. Columns 12 and 13 only need to be completed for zero slack paths

activities lead from the event, then dependent and independent activities should be segregated, and the resulting events connected by dummy activities

(e) No given event can be followed by an activity path which leads back to that event.

TIME ESTIMATES

When the activities have been defined, *time estimates* can be prepared in the manner described in Chapter 6. It is the function of PERT to take into account the areas of uncertainty, and this is done by forecasting the three time estimates: optimistic (a), most likely (m) and pessimistic (b).

Assuming that these three time estimates are connected in the form of a unimodal probability distribution, which may be skew, a possible model is the 'beta distribution'; this was chosen by the original PERT team[3, 4] to determine the *most probable, mean* or *expected time* (t_e) and the *standard deviation* (σ). (The most probable time represents that time where there is a 50-50 chance that completion will be earlier or later; the standard deviation (σ) or the variance (σ^2) indicates the dispersion of the probability distribution, that is, the range of uncertainty.) Making certain simplifying assumptions, the following formulae were derived:

$$t_e = \frac{a+4m+b}{6}$$

$$\sigma = \frac{b-a}{6}$$

$$\sigma^2 = \left(\frac{b-a}{6}\right)^2$$

It has since been shown[5] that for the three time estimates, the possible net error is $1 \cdot 6\%$ of the range. The effect of this error, together with those due to the assumptions made in deriving the formulae, can result in cumulative errors to the expected time and standard deviation of 7% and 4% of the range respectively.

With the expected time for each activity entered on the network, the *earliest expected event time*, and the *latest allowable event time* can be calculated for each event. The earliest expected event time (T_E) is found by taking the longest time path from the start of the network to that event; the latest allowable event time (T_L), which is the latest date on which an event can occur without creating a delay in the programme, is the longest time path from that event to the last objective event, that is:

$T_E = \Sigma t_e$ maximum on any path, from the start of the programme to that event

$T_L = T_D$ for last event $- \Sigma t_e$ maximum on any path from that event to last event

T_D is the directed date for completion of a programme; (if this is not given, $T_D = T_L$ for the end event).

The event variance associated with T_E will be the sum of the variances along the path taken in calculating T_E:

$$(\sigma)_E^2 = \Sigma\sigma^2 \text{ on } T_E \text{ path}$$

The event variance associated with T_L is found by fixing the variance for the last event at zero and summing the variances along the T_L path.

ANALYSIS AND REPLANNING

One of the most important aspects of PERT is the *slack* path analysis that is carried out for events and activities.

Event slack (S_E) is defined as the difference between the latest allowable date and the expected date for a particular event expressed in weeks:

$$S_E = T_L - T_E$$

A *critical path* in the network is that path where the slack for any event on it is zero, thus the path itself is said to have zero slack, and sub-critical paths can be classified by their slack value.

When a scheduled *objective date* (T_S) is given for an event, then if this date is earlier than T_L, it is used in lieu; the slack then becomes:

$$S'_E = T_S - T_E$$

Both T_L and the slack for all precursor events will be affected. The slack may become negative if T_S is earlier than T_E, and the critical path may have negative slack.

After the event slack has been calculated for each event, analysis is carried out in four ways:

(a) *Slack order*. Events and their associated slack are tabulated in order from the largest negative slack through zero to the largest positive slack. This will show all the paths of the network in their order of criticality

(b) *Event order*. Used as a cross reference for checking

(c) *Expected date*. Events are ordered in accordance with their calendar sequence, together with scheduled dates if given

(d) *Latest date*. Events ordered similarly to (c). This will indicate where T_S has to be substituted for T_L.

Activity slack (S_A) can differ from event slack, and is defined as the difference between the latest allowable date of the successor event, and the expected completion date of the activity:

$$S_A = T_L \text{ (successor)} - [T_E \text{ (predecessor)} + t_e]$$

This is sometimes called the *primary slack* or *total float** to differentiate

102

it from the *secondary slack* (S'_A) or *free float** which represents the amount of time an activity can be delayed from its earliest start time without affecting the earliest start time of the successor event:

$$S'_A = T_E \text{ (successor)} - (T_E \text{ (predecessor)} + t_e)$$

The activities may be analysed in a similar manner to the events, but in the slack order report, the secondary slack should be included as it is important in the scheduling process.

With the concept of slack, must be associated the probability of accomplishing each activity. One method of doing this is to rank paths in terms of the probability of positive slack.[6] This is illustrated in Fig. 7.3, where the probability distributions of T_E and T_L overlap; normal

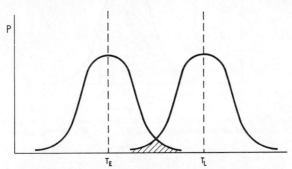

Fig. 7.3. Probability of positive slack
Shaded area = probability of no positive slack (P_{NS})
Probability of positive slack (P_S) = $1 - P_{NS}$

distributions are assumed when the shaded area indicates the probability of no positive slack, hence the probability of positive slack is unity minus this figure. A simpler method is to order activities in terms of primary slack, and within this order rank them according to the value of the standard deviation. Then, if the slack equals:

0·0000	there is a 1 in 2	chance that $(t_e + \text{slack})$ will be exceeded
0·6745σ	there is a 1 in 4	chance that $(t_e + \text{slack})$ will be exceeded
1σ	there is a 1 in 6	chance that $(t_e + \text{slack})$ will be exceeded
2σ	there is a 1 in 364	chance that $(t_e + \text{slack})$ will be exceeded
3σ	there is a 1 in 7400	chance that $(t_e + \text{slack})$ will be exceeded

Where there is a scheduled date (T_S), the probability of this being achieved can be determined in a similar manner, or the value can be obtained from Fig. 7.4. The extent of a possible time slip is perhaps of more practical importance and for such purposes the maximum value can be taken to be:

$$T_E + 3\sigma_{T_E} - T_S$$

*These terms are used in the *Critical Path Method* (C.P.M.) which was developed independently of PERT. It uses the same network techniques, but as it is a time/cost method applicable when there is little uncertainty, it is not described in this book.

103

The network must therefore be replanned in order to:

(a) Remove negative slack
(b) Allocate positive slack to give maximum probability of accomplishment, and of meeting scheduled date or dates
(c) Introduce slack into those paths where the risk margin is high, that is, there is a high value of standard deviation
(d) Investigate critical and sub-critical paths, to ensure that no high risk activities are included; or, if this is unavoidable, to ensure

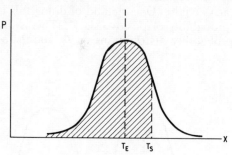

Fig. 7.4. *Probability of meeting a scheduled date.*
The probability is given by the shaded area. This can be determined from probability tables in terms of the standard deviate:

$$\frac{T_S - T_E}{\sigma_{T_E}}$$

that the management is aware of the risks and the possible effect of overruns on the network, e.g. the possibility of a sub-critical path becoming the critical path.

These requirements may be met by one or a combination of actions:

(a) Increase resources to susceptible activities
(b) Reallocate resources between activities
(c) Change series activities to parallel or ladder. *Ladder* activities are those that progressively feed to, or are progressively fed from, other activities
(d) Delete activities.

To achieve the optimum plan, the analyst may carry out a number of simulation exercises to determine the effects of introducing changes and overruns; hence replanning will be a reiterative process.

The final network may be converted into a calendar or 'squared' format, a version of which is shown in Fig. 7.5. Alternatively, or in addition, the network may be divided horizontally into areas of responsibility as shown in Fig. 7.6. Gantt or bar charts may also be prepared.

SCHEDULING

Although scheduled or directed dates must be taken into account when constructing a network based on a programme work breakdown, the final step must be the conversion of the network into a calendar based *schedule*, which will ensure that resources and facilities are available when required. Scheduling will affect costs, and the factors to be considered are:

(a) The availability of the required manpower, equipment and facilities during specific calendar periods
(b) The minimising of premium costs and idle time for manpower, equipment and facilities
(c) Funding limitations
(d) The manager's judgement as to what is a reasonable time to allow for performing the work. (This could be t_e plus the margin risk considered adequate.)

The result will be the establishment of a *scheduled elapsed time* (t_S) for an activity, which may or may not be equal to t_e. Following this, the

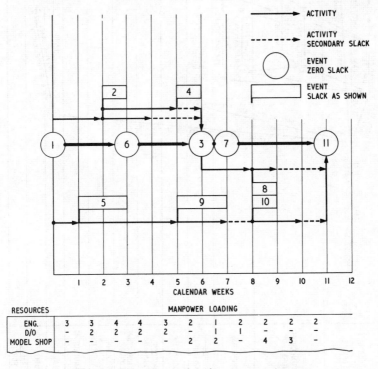

Fig. 7.5. Squared network and resource requirements

earliest completion date (S_E) and the *latest completion date* (S_L) for each activity can be derived by summing t_S as t_e was summed to give T_E and T_L, and then converting to a calendar date. These dates may in turn give rise to a *scheduled completion date* (T_S) for an event or activity, this being the date assigned by the manager for completion; if this date is not specified, T_S is taken as S_E. The *directed date* (T_D) is a date established by a higher authority.

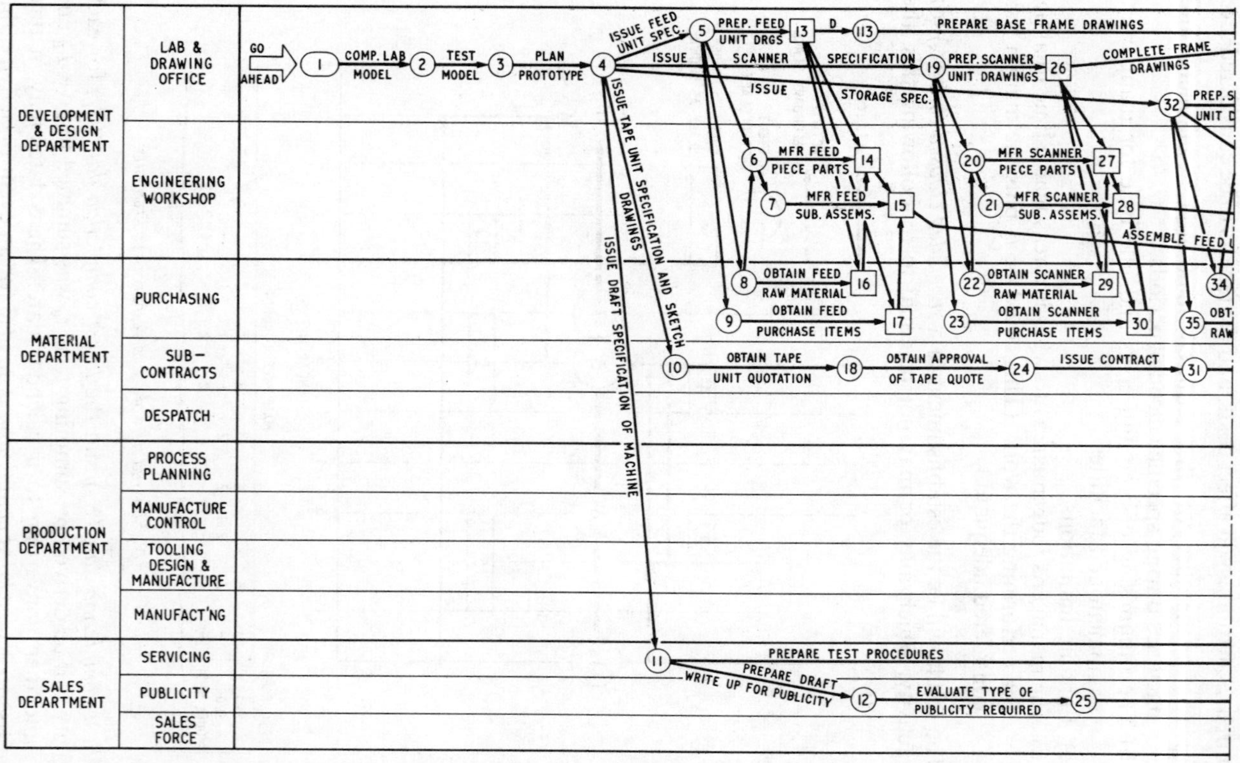

Fig. 7.6. Network showing areas of responsibility. Reproduced from 1900 Series PERT (1966) by courtesy of International Computers and Tabulators Limited

For *programme management*, the *schedule network* or the *operating programme management network* may be given in summary form, which corresponds to the levels of the work breakdown summary.

The summary form is derived from the detail network by:

(a) Summarising individual detail networks
(b) Integrating the individual summarised networks
(c) Including all interface events and milestones.

It will be seen in Chapter 8 that the requirements of United Kingdom Government departments are limited to the work breakdown network, whilst those of the United States Government agencies will call for the management network in association with PERT/COST information. One reason for this is the more universal use of computers in the United States. (The implementation of the procedures mentioned makes this imperative.) It is also the policy in the United States not to call for more detailed information than is necessary, by assuming that the information which feeds into the top level reports is processed correctly.

RESOURCE ALLOCATION

An important adjunct of PERT is *resource allocation* or *manpower loading*; this is of use in a single project for scheduling purposes, and also when a number of projects are involved.[7]

At some stage during the replanning of the network, the skills required during each weekly period for each activity should be summarised as shown in Fig. 7.5. Wide variations in loading are undesirable, and requirements must be within the effort available at that time.

As discussed in Chapter 6, the estimate should have been prepared on the basis of the utilisation of staff expected to be available unless an earlier scheduled date has been specified, necessitating extra resources. In the latter event, attempts should be made to transfer the required skills from concurrent activities, that is transposing such activities to earlier or later stages or extending their duration, before considering the employment of additional staff. Fluctuations in number of staff may be compensated for by varying the position of slack in the paths, although the prime consideration should be the risk associated with an activity.

As with all other aspects of project control, resource allocation must be a continuous function. Particular skills may not be available as required due to overruns on other activities, sickness, resignations; conversely, extra staff may become available due to activities finishing early, or the shut down of other projects. Hence, the network will require continuous up-dating.

For a particular network the resources may always be aggregated, but it is rarely possible to optimise the network for resources without a computer, due to the number of possible permutations that can arise in permuting the slack, or even by splitting activities. Resource allocation then becomes part of the scheduling activity.[8, 9]

R & D Administration

REFERENCES

1. MARSHALL, A. W., MECKLING, W. H., *Predictability of the Cost, Time and Success of Development*, RAND Corporation Report P-1821, December (1959)
2. PECK, M. J., SCHERER, F. M., *The Weapons Acquisition Process: An Economic Analysis*, Division of Research, Graduate School of Business Administration, Harvard University, Cambridge, Mass. (1962)
3. *PERT, Summary Report Phase I*, Navy Special Projects Office, U.S. Government Printing Office (1960)
4. KELLY, J., 'Critical path planning and scheduling: mathematical basis' *Operations Res.*, **9**, No. 3, p. 296 (1961)
5. MACCRIMMON C. R., RYAVEC, C. A., *An Analytical Study of the PERT assumptions*, RAND Corporation Memo. RM-3408-PR, December (1962)
6. *Planning and Control Techniques for Project Management*, Vol. II U.S. Army Material Command Regulation 11-16, August (1963)
7. MCGEE, A. A., MARKARIAN, M. D., 'Optimum allocation of research/engineering manpower within a multi-project organisational structure', *IRE Trans. Engng. Mgmt.*, **EM-9**, No. 3, p. 104 (1962)
8. NORDEN, P. V., 'Resource usage and network planning techniques', Chapter 5, *Operations Research in Research and Development*', Ed. Dean, B. V., John Wiley Inc., NY (1963)
9. *RAMPS (Resource Allocation and Multiprojects Scheduling System) Training Text and Users Guide*, CEIR Inc., NY (1962)

BIBLIOGRAPHY

EISNER, H., 'A generalised network approach to the planning and scheduling of a research program', *Operations Res.*, **10**, No. 1, p. 115 (1962)
POCOCK, J. W., 'PERT as an analytical aid for program planning—its payoffs and problems', *Operations Res.*, **10**, No. 6, p. 893, (1962)
ASHLEY, W. F., AUSTIN, M. I., 'Case studies in network planning, scheduling and control of R & D projects', Chapter 12, *Operations Research in Research and Development*, Ed. Dean, B. V., John Wiley Inc., NY (1963)
MALCOLM, D. G., 'Integrated research and development management systems', Chapter 4, *Operations Research in Research and Development*, Ed. Dean, B. V., John Wiley Inc., NY (1963)
MILLER, R. W., *Schedule, Cost and Profit Control with PERT*, McGraw-Hill Inc. NY (1963)
PERT/TIME System Description Manual, Air Force Systems Command, June (1963)
STIRES, D. M., MURPHY, M. M., *PERT/CPM*, Industrial Education International (1963)
WOODGATE, H. S., *Planning by Network*, Business Publications, London (1963)
JOHNSON, E. J., 'PERT/PMD—project monitoring device', *IEEE Trans. Engng. Mgmt.*, **EM-11**, No. 2, p. 82 (1964)
ROSENBLOOM, R. S., 'Notes on the development of network models for resource allocation in R & D projects', *IEEE Trans. Engng. Mgmt.*, **EM-11**, No. 2, p. 58 (1964)
SMITH, K. M., *A Practical Guide to Network Planning*, British Institute of Management (1965)

Chapter 8

Communication and Control

Planning and estimating are forecasting processes which indicate what will probably occur as the logical result of decisions made; as such, they are solely an aid to the *control* of R & D. It is the act of decision making that constitutes the *project control function*, and to be effective there must be rapid communication of the necessary information.

Since there must be nearly as many control systems as there are R & D organisations, this chapter formulates a theoretical basis for the project control function. Financial and Government control requirements are also discussed and an integrated system is proposed for the rapid communication of information.

CONCEPT OF CONTROL

Using the operations research methodology developed by Ackoff[1, 2], let:

I = a group leader

L_i = an expenditure, e.g. effort, money
($i = 1, 2, \ldots m$)

O_j = an outcome, i.e. a result of an expenditure L_i in following a course of action C
($j = 1, 2, \ldots n$)

C = the course of action, i.e. the set of variables other than the group leader and the expenditure that can affect the outcome.

The expenditures and outcomes may be considered as forming exclusive and exhaustive sets, that is, one expenditure can result in one and only one outcome. This does not mean, however, that the selection of a second expenditure cannot result in the same outcome. The validity of this assumption can be shown by considering two outcomes, O' and O'', which are not exclusive and exhaustive, when by means of the Boolean expansion they can be formed into the following set of four exclusive and exhaustive outcomes:

$$O_1 = O' \text{ and } O''$$
$$O_2 = O' \text{ and not } O''$$
$$O_3 = \text{not } O' \text{ but } O''$$
$$O_4 = \text{neither } O' \text{ nor } O''$$

An activity, that is, a particular job of work, may then be defined by three parameters:

$P_i = P(L_i/IC)$ = the probability* that the group leader *I* will incur an expenditure L_i in following a course of action *C*

$E_{ij} = P(O_j/L_iIC)$ = the probability* that outcome O_j will occur if the group leader *I* incurs an expenditure L_i in following a course of action *C*, i.e. the efficiency of L_i for O_j in C

U_j = the utility (relative value) of outcome O_j to group leader *I* for course of action *C*.

Then since the expenditures and outcomes have been defined as forming exhaustive and exclusive sets, the sum of the probabilities of choice over the set of expenditures must be equal to unity; and the sum of the efficiencies of any expenditure over the set of outcomes must also equal unity. That is:

$$\sum_{i=1}^{m} P_i = 1 \text{ and } \sum_{j=1}^{n} E_{ij} = 1$$

If L_x is defined as the most probable expenditure, then the probability that the group leader will incur an expenditure up to that value is:

$$\sum_{i=1}^{x} P_i = \tfrac{1}{2} \text{ by definition of most probable.}$$

If the activity is feasible or deemed to be so, then the sum of the efficiences must equal or approach unity, that is:

$$\sum_{j=1}^{y} E_{ij} \to 1 \text{ since } y \to n \text{ as all outcomes must be achievable.}$$

The utility or relative value U_j can be equated to the design specification; let:

$$\sum_{j=1}^{n} U_j = S \text{ where } S \geqq 0$$

The *expected achievement* (*A*) can then be defined as:

$$A = \sum_i \sum_j P_i E_{ij} U_j$$

the value of which can range from a minimum of zero, where the group

*Even though an R & D activity is perhaps the most clearly unique (non-repeated) of productive activities, probabilities in the sense of personal degrees of belief can be attached to development outcomes.[3]

leader will fail, to a maximum of S, where he will obtain everything of value. At the start of the activity the value may be given by:

$$A_x = \sum_{i=1}^{x} \sum_{j=1}^{y} P_i \, E_{ij} \, U_j \rightarrow \frac{S}{2} \text{ for the most probable expenditure.}$$

The above argument has been limited to 'activities' as this is the level at which project control is exercised. It is also applicable to the project as a whole, but it should be noted that the project 'expected achievement' may be derived from the product of all the 'expected achievements' of all the activities, whether dependent or independent, that is:

$$A_x = A_{x_1} \, A_{x_2} \, A_{x_3} \dots A_{x_2}$$

If this formulation is used, S_x may also be used as a 'weighting factor'.

This definition of achievement refers to a particular group leader I, expenditure L_x, course of action C, outcome O_y, and specification of value S. Hence in the course of the activity, if A does not increase from the initial value, action must be taken to change one or more of these parameters.

The group leader may fail owing to lack of knowledge or experience, or he may deviate from the planned course of action. Assistance by the project manager can introduce a correcting factor.

As the undetermined elements of the activity become defined and solved, the risk margin will be reduced and this will be reflected by revised estimates. Approval may have to be 'sought for an increased figure in order to increase the value of A. This will most probably occur if the outcomes are not forthcoming, although an alternative solution might be to modify the required outcomes, or, what is usually more practical, to depreciate the specification, that is, reduce the value of S when the probability of expenditure and efficiency will increase.

Finally there is the course of action C, which can only be changed by following a new course of action; this implies a *cut-off* decision. From the above argument, this decision should be taken immediately the value of A starts to decrease, and there is no acceptable method of arresting this fall.

Summarising, the possible decisions that constitute the control function are:

(a) Assist or replace project leader
(b) Authorise a change in expenditure
(c) Modify desired outcomes, i.e. objectives
(d) Amend specification
(e) Cut-off activity.

To know when such decisions must be made, there must be immediate information of any deviation from:

(a) Planned course of action
(b) Planned expenditure.

To help ensure that the correct decision is made, forecasts will have to be amended in the light of new knowledge available:

(a) Anticipated expenditure
(b) Plan of work, assuming no change in course of action.

To obtain and record this information a certain amount of paperwork and routine will be necessary. As the cost accounts and other interested parties need the same basic facts, their requirements will be discussed before an integrated system is proposed.

FINANCIAL CONTROL

It is the function of the accounts department to maintain accurate records of the costs incurred on a project. This is part of the normal accountancy process and is discussed in Chapter 13. The financial manager must also ensure that the money allocated to a project is spent in accordance with the approved budget, which incorporates the project estimate; if not, finance may not be available as and when required. A change in the pattern of expenditure can affect the potential profitability of the project, as shown in Chapter 5. This oversighting procedure is termed *financial control*, but does not constitute project control, as defined in the previous section, although managements may confuse them.

Financial control may be defined as 'the comparison of actual costs with forecast (i.e. estimated) costs over a defined period'.[4] The starting point is therefore the estimate, and for all costs incurred there must be a proper system of coding and classification so that they can be related to the estimate. As the estimate is in terms of *committed expenditure*, and suppliers' invoices may not be received until a later date, it follows that parallel accounts of committed and *actual* expenditure should be kept. To avoid duplicate posting, and the errors that may arise therefrom, these parallel accounts should be maintained by the responsible department, that is, accounts. This procedure ensures that confidential matters, such as salaries, contingencies, are not divulged unnecessarily. The basic records from which project accounts are prepared, for example, time sheets, requisitions, invoices, will be used for other accounts such as salaries, stock, bought ledger; for auditing purposes, these records must be filed so as to ensure easy location from any account, and there must be cross referencing from the various accounts. In consequence the accounting procedure, though of no direct concern to the R & D worker, must nevertheless be understood by the manager.

CONTROL OF UNITED KINGDOM GOVERNMENT CONTRACTS

In the United Kingdom, a Government or nationalised industry R & D contract normally stipulates that the work must be done to the satisfaction of the Technical Director of the department concerned. It is the responsibility of this officer or his appointed delegate to agree a *speci-fication* and plan of work with the contractor, to initiate contractual changes, and to maintain technical control. It should be noted that only the contracts branch that issued the contract can instruct the contractor to carry out any work not described in the original contract, unless the contract specifically includes a clause to the effect 'or as authorised by . . .'. If a D.C.P. (Chapter 6) has been requested, he will comment as necessary, and keep a watching brief on the expenditure by means of the following documents which the contractor must provide:

(a) A monthly *return of expenditure* within two weeks of the end of the period. This return calls for labour, overheads, and material expended during the period, together with the cumulative total, and is normally made on an official form

(b) A quarterly *return of costs* within four weeks of the end of the period. This return should be broken down into the same areas of effort as the development cost plan, and give both estimated and actual sums for the quarter, together with the cumulative expenditure. The latest estimates must also be given in a similar form to the D.C.P., that is, for the following quarters, half years and years to completion. If network techniques are used, the revised network is also required

(c) A completely revised D.C.P. annually, or as required by the Technical Director, or if major changes arise in the technical plan

(d) *Progress reports* at regular intervals.

In a *cost plus contract* the final accounts will be vetted by the relevant Government accounts department, who will be responsible for agreeing these accounts, and also the overhead rates, with the contractors' accounts department.

In certain contracts, the contracts department or accounts department of any Ministry may instruct the Technical Costs Directorate of the Ministry of Technology to oversee the work. The duties of this department are to ensure that all expenditure, both in terms of effort and money, has been properly incurred, and that the Government is receiving value for money. They may comment on the firm's estimates if they consider the firm has under- or over-estimated. They may also assist the contracts branch in fixing prices, advising on wage rates to be applied, and aid the accounts branch in agreeing overheads. In pursuit of this they require an accurate allocation of costs to the work packages, together with all the information on which the contractor compiled his estimate. In accordance with the *Standard Conditions of Government Contracts* (see Chapter 10) they can call for work sheets, invoices, and other evidence in support of the contractor's claims.

To summarise, the records required will be those that should be maintained by the contractor's accounts department, with the proviso that there must be accurate booking to work packages, and that the supporting evidence for the booking must be readily available. Expenditure must also be related to estimates and progress by means of reports or otherwise.

Common Report Heading

Project	Reporting origin	Contract No.	Report dates
Level/summary item			Term (span): Cut-off date: Release date:

(a) Management Summary Report

Item level summary no.	Cost of work						Schedule			Total Item Critical Item
	Work performed to date			Totals at completion			Most critical slack weeks	Compl. date	Sched. completion date S — Sched. A — Actual ,, E — Earliest ,, L — Latest ,,	
	Value	Act. cost	(Overrun) underrun	Planned cost	Latest revised est.	Projected (overrun) underrun			P yr. 1966 JFMAMJJASOND 1967 JFMAMJJASOND L yr.	

(b) Project Status Report

Identification				Time status			Cost of work					
Item charge or summary no.	Level	First event no.	Last event no.	Sched. or act (A) compl. date	Earliest and latest compl. date	Most critical slack (wks.)	Work performed to date			Totals at completion		
							Value	Actual cost	(Overrun) underrun	Planned cost	Latest revised est.	Projected (overrun) underrun

(c) Organisation Status Report

Identification				Man-hours				Direct costs				Time	
				Work to date	Totals at completion			Work to date	Totals at completion				
Item charge no.	Responsible organisation	Performing organisation	Res. code	Actual	Planned	Latest revised est.	Projected (overrun) underrun	Actual	Planned	Latest revised est.	Projected (overrun) underrun	Most critical slack (wks.)	Sched. or act (A) compl. date

(d) Financial Plan and Status Report

Charge no.	Month	Incremental cost				Cumulative cost			
		Planned	Latest revised estimates	Actual	(Over) under plan	Planned	Actual	Latest revised estimate	(Over) under plan

(e) Manpower Loading Report by Resource. Month

Identification				Man-hours				Time
Month	Res. (skill) code	Perf. orgn.	Charge no.	Planned	Actual	Latest revised est.	(Over) under plan	Most critical slack (wks.)

Fig. 8.1. PERT/COST *output reports*

(continued overleaf)

(f) Cost Category Status Report

Identification	Man-hours					Total cost				
	To date		Totals at completion			To date		Totals at completion		
Cost category	Planned	Actual	Planned	Latest revised estimate	Projected (overrun) underrun	Planned	Actual	Planned	Latest revised estimate	Projected (overrun) underrun

(g) Work Package/Activity Report

Activity				Completion date			Activity slack $S_L - S_E$
Pred. events	Succ. events	Description	Schd. elapsed time	Expected S_E	Latest S_L	Schd. or actual	

(h) Summary Financial Forecast

Identification		Actual prior	Forecast Months/Years									
Summary item/ cost category	Level		Current	+1	+2	+3	+4	+5	+6	+7	Total to complete	Total

Fig. 8.1. (continued)

Last but not least, all expenditure must be shown to have been properly authorised under the terms of the contract.

PERT/COST

With the depth of planning required to make PERT successful, it is logical that the estimates should be integrated with this procedure. This is done in the reporting technique termed PERT/COST which is approved by the United States Department of Defence for use by contractors.

With this technique, although the need for the individual estimating of activities is still required, the reporting level is that of the work package which is defined as 'the unit of work required to complete a specific job or process, such as a report, a design, a document, a piece of hardware, or a service, for which a single person or organisation is responsible'. This definition corresponds to the end item sub-divisions of the work breakdown summary, although these may be split into a number of work packages in order to limit their value and extent in time. A work package may, therefore, consist either of a single activity or of a related group of activities.

Summary numbers are given to each work package to assist in accumulating or summarising costs for each sub-division in the programme breakdown. Such numbers are shown in Fig. 6.2 and Fig. 6.3, the first digit denoting divisions on the first level, the second sub-divisions on the second, and so on. These numbers do not necessarily replace the *charge numbers* that may be assigned by the contractor in accordance with his costing system for activities or tasks (see p. 122), but the two must be reconcilable.

The input information required to operate the PERT/COST procedure may be summarised as follows:

(a) PERT/TIME input
(b) Work breakdown structure
(c) Activity to charge number identification
(d) Charge to summary number identification
(e) Cost estimates
(f) Actual costs
(g) Budget authorisation
(h) Wages and salaries payable
(i) Manpower bill/rainbow category
(j) Resource code/cost category.

This information will provide the following computer outputs, the approved format for the principal being shown in Fig. 8.1:

(a) *Management summary*. This is the top management report showing the cost of 'work performed to date' and 'totals at completion', together with the schedule for each of the major items within the

117

programme based on specific levels of the work breakdown structure. The concept of 'value of work performed' is a function of the total actual costs and revised estimates to completion; its purpose is to assess whether work packages will keep within the estimate. This report may be supplemented by the *problem analysis report*, which is a written report giving an analysis of tasks where problems exist, the impact on other areas, and action taken

(b) *Programme/project status report.* This contains the information from which the management summary report is compiled

(c) *Organisation status report.* This is functionally orientated and gives the information required at work package level

(d) *Financial plan and status report.* This is primarily for the Accountant and controller, showing incremental and cumulative costs

(e) *Manpower loading report.* This is ancillary to resource allocation, which was discussed in Chapter 7

(f) *Cost category status report.* Shows the costs related to functions

(g) *Work package/activity report.* Identifies all activities associated with a specific charge number together with the time data

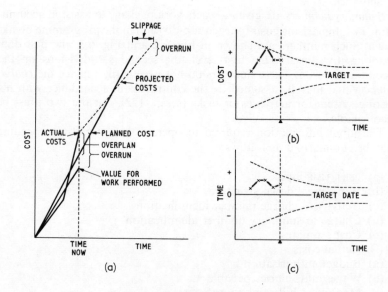

Fig. 8.2. PERT/COST graphical displays
(a) Cost of work report
(b) Cost outlook report
(c) Schedule outlook report

(i) *Rainbow category report.* Identifies manpower loading for various levels of the summary within the programme. (This report is not illustrated as it is only used occasionally)

(j) *Summary financial forecast.* Gives the actual and estimated (or planned) costs grouped by summary item or cost category for months or years.

The information contained in these computer reports may be displayed graphically. The following examples are illustrated in Fig. 8.2:

(a) *Cost of work report.* Gives the information contained in the financial plan, status report and management summary report; 'value for work performed' is also included
(b) *Cost outlook report.* Shows the cost trends for completion at any given level or summary item. Limit lines may be introduced as shown
(c) *Schedule outlook report.* Shows the time trends to complete in a similar manner to the cost outlook report.

AUTHORISATION OF EXPENDITURE

The procedure for obtaining project approval was discussed in Chapter 5; *authorisation*, which is the responsibility of the research director or manager, follows when contractual and financial arrangements are finalised and resources become available. Officially, authorisation means the issue of a *project order* giving instruction to proceed with part or all the programme of work planned and estimated, together with a *cost code* showing how the expenditure must be charged. Authorisation should not be interpreted as a licence to spend money up to some limit before asking for more; expenditure can only arise from the plan of work, and it is the plan, either in total or in part, that is authorised. The format of the project order should highlight this fact, and this can be done by using the same layout as the front of the estimated project costs form, showing the expenditure authorised during any period for each task and activity, (Fig. 8.3). It should be noted that authorisation for any special expenditure approved, such as for capital equipment or special layouts, should be issued at the same time, but this will involve a different procedure.

Authorisation of expenditure implies a system of identifying all expenditure incurred; to be effective, this must be capable of being followed rigidly without time consuming paperwork or creating petty annoyance. The simplest method of identification is to give each work package a separate number. The number, however, may be used to convey information, as in the following example:

(a) First prefix letter denotes customer, e.g.
G = Government (direct)
I = Government (indirect)
C = commercial
P = private
R = recoverable from production
S = services to sales

119

Note: If costs are not derived directly
from activity estimate, identify and
detail changes on reverse.   AUTHORI

Task No.	Activity No.	Description and Remarks	Cost Heading	Actual Costs Committed	Quar
			Total		
			Total		
			Total		
			Total		
			Total		
			Grand Totals		

RS No.	Project	Custom

Fig. 8.3. Standard form

ECT COSTS (direct labour, materials and overheads)

Issue No.
Revised

				Estimates				
rter	Quarter	Quarter	Half Year	Half Year	Year	Year	Year	Total
				Project No.			Sheet No.	
							Of	

rised project costs

(b) Second prefix letter to denote method of recovery
    F = fixed price
    L = cost plus (authorised limit)
    A = price to be agreed
    O = overhead charge
(c) Third prefix letter
    R = research
    D = product development
    P = process development
    A = application investigation
(d) First number, or block of numbers to denote project. If there are several laboratories, each laboratory can have a block of numbers. The numbers issued serially in each block denote the laboratory having the overall responsibility for the project
(e) Second number, or block, to denote item of contract, or task which is part of a contract item
(f) Third number, or block, for work package. If PERT/COST is used this is termed the charge number, and is associated with the summary number. These are assigned to each end item sub-division of the work breakdown structure, and arranged so that costs can be accumulated readily for each sub-division at each level (see p. 117)
(g) If there are a number of activities within a work package, these may be identified by a letter, or by precursor and successor events.

An example of the above system could be:

GLD 2456 012 3435X

This would be interpreted as: direct Government contract, cost plus, product development. Laboratory 2 in overall charge, serial project number 456, item 12 (or task 12) of the project work package identified by precursor event 34 and successor event 35—the letter X denotes that the work package is a single activity.

In addition to specific project orders, the system must also accommodate possible standing orders for services that cannot be charged directly to a project and may in fact be charged to overheads, for example:

(a) Technical services to production or sales
(b) Minor experimental work
(c) Licensor and licensee technical liaison
(d) Compilation of manuals, reports
(e) Maintenance of drawings.

Using the above system we could have:

SDA 3000 091 17

This would denote services to sales, overhead charge, application, investigation, laboratory or drawing office number 3, standing order 091 (which should have a financial limit), job (i.e. activity) number 17.

BOOKING OF EFFORT

A common method of booking time in an R & D laboratory is by use of a *weekly time sheet*, Fig. 8.4. Such a sheet is completed each week by every worker, who enters both the job number and hours worked. It is obvious, however, that a numbering system such as that described above would not be satisfactory, particularly if there were a large number of activities in a project. Even if the worker remembered the right number, he might write it incorrectly; but equally, if he did not know the number

								w/e
WEEKLY TIME SHEET					H			For accnts, use
NAME		No.			Section No.			
Job or Project No.	M	T	W	Th.	F		Total Hours	
Signature..................................... Approved..								

Fig. 8.4. Weekly time sheet

he might put down anything on the basis of 'so what—it is being charged to a project'. Apart from making the cost numbering system so simple that it is virtually useless, the alternative is to ensure that the cost code number does not concern the R & D worker, and this can be achieved by the *job ticket* system, similar to that used in factory production.

When a project is authorised, all staff participating in the work will be issued with an *activity instruction card*, Fig. 8.5, for each activity or work

ACTIVITY INSTRUCTION CARD

Project		Activity Cost Code	
Activity/Work Package		Cost Allocation	/
Instructions		Person	

Expected Start Date	Expected Finish Date		Total Man/Weeks		

Week		Mon.	Tue.	Wed.	Thur.	Fri.	Total	Lab. Book		Remarks
No.	End							No.	Page	

Fig. 8.5. Activity instruction card

124

package concerning them. For the staff member, this will be his written instructions to do a specific job. It should show the expected dates of commencing and completing the activity together with man-weeks scheduled. (The information on the activity instruction card can assist in resource allocation, which was discussed in Chapter 7.) Little effort is needed to complete such a form, and by entering a laboratory note-book reference, identification is made with the work. In the remarks column the worker can note requests for extra time, causes of delay, such as materials not forthcoming, etc. When the work is completed, the card may be retained by the project office as a permanent record. When such a system is used, it must be remembered that a proportion of each person's time will be chargeable to overheads, (holidays, sickness, attending conferences); a separate card must be provided on which such times can be entered, to provide a means by which the accountants can balance the salary accounts.

The activity instruction card has two further advantages. First, work cannot be booked, and therefore charged, until it is duly authorised; secondly, in a functional or discipline orientated organisation, the cards can be passed via the departmental head, and, on completion of the work, returned through him, thus permitting stricter staff control.

The cards must be examined weekly by a clerk, who will enter on a *labour analysis sheet* (Fig. 8.6) the total hours worked against the *cost allocation number*, which denotes grade of effort and salary number of each person authorised to work on that activity. These numbers can be entered in their respective groups at the start of the activity so that a check is provided against bookings by an unauthorised person.

From the labour analysis (hours), the total effort of each grade of staff can be summed, and entered for the period in the 'actual' (A) rows of the *estimate and progress record*, (Fig. 6.4, p. 76), for that activity. The labour analysis can then be passed to the accounts for extending the hours to money by applying the actual salaries paid; the results are entered on a duplicate form, labour analysis—salaries.

Such a system is relatively foolproof, and warrants respect because it makes little demand on scientific staff—an important consideration. Another advantage is that in the event of a postmortem, the staff engaged on any particular activity can be identified, and their notebooks will show the work done in any period. Furthermore, both the project control and accounts obtain their information from the same record, so that any discrepancies can be due only to posting errors, which should be traced easily. Last but not least, salaries remain confidential.

PROVISIONING DIRECT MATERIALS

The project order will be the authority for the purchase of all direct materials needed to carry out the plan of work and shown in the build up of the estimate, unless exclusions have been made. For these materials no further authorisation should be necessary, it being left to the project

125

LABOUR ANALYSIS—HOURS/SALARIES | ACTIVITY COST CODE

Cost Allocation	Year Wk B/F	1/27	2/28	3/29	4/30	5/31	6/32	7/33	8/34	9/35	10/36	11/37	12/39	13/40	Cum. Total C/F
Total															
Total															
Grand Total															
Cum. Total															

Fig. 8.6. Labour analysis sheet

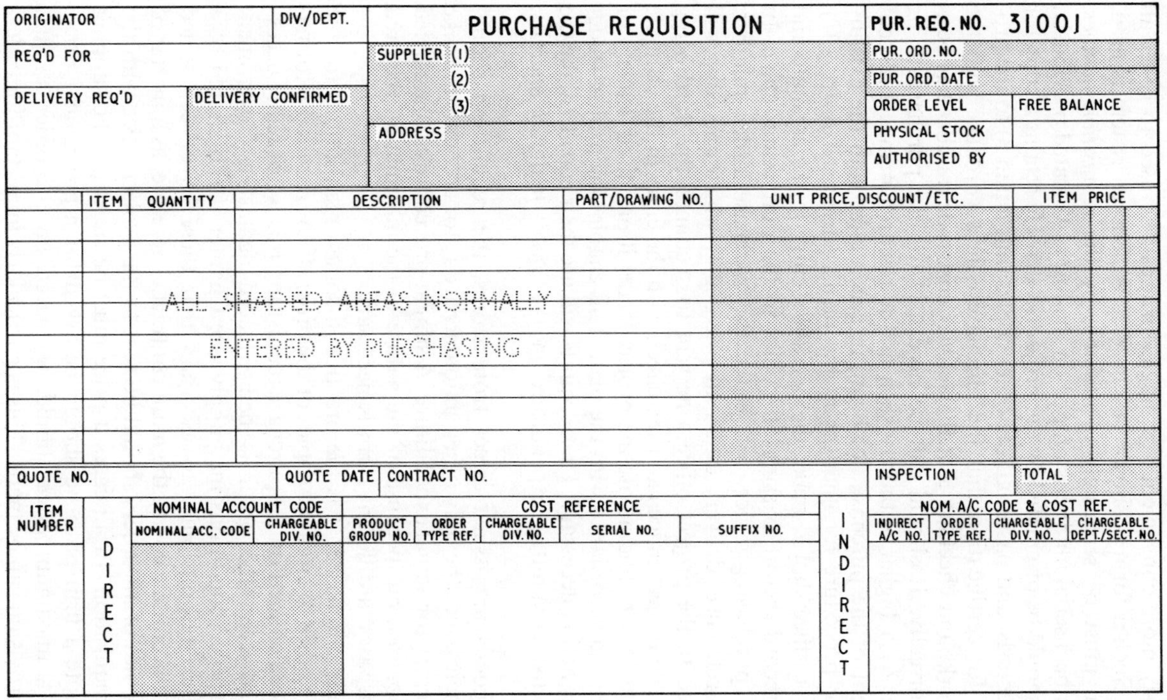

Fig. 8.7. Purchase requisition form. Courtesy: Elliott Brothers (London) Limited

leader to initiate, by means of *requisitions*, the necessary orders.

Companies may have different forms for material drawn from stores, purchases from outside suppliers, interdepartmental orders, etc., but it is obviously more convenient if a single form can be used to cover all purposes. Such a form is shown in Fig. 8.7. Whichever system is used, each form must be separately identifiable by the *requisition number*, which can be a serial number stamped on the form. As stated previously, the form should be originated by the project leader. He retains a copy for his own records, and passes all the other copies (minimum 3) to the project office for certification that the purchase is in accordance with the plan of work, and checking that the activity cost code number has been entered correctly. It should not be necessary for the purchase to be authorised by a higher authority such as the research manager, except in the event of the purchase not being in accordance with the existing plan. (The procedure for changes in the plan is discussed on p. 131). The project office should make the necessary entry in the estimate and progress record, before passing all copies to the purchasing office. In turn, the purchasing office will enter the purchase order number, supplier's reference, delivery date and price, after which one copy will be returned to the project office, one sent to accounts, the third being retained. The project office can then check with the entry in the estimate and progress record and advise the project leader if promised delivery or price are not in accordance with the plan. This enables the project leader to take any action necessary. The accounts will use their copy to make the entry against committed expenditure in the *direct material analysis*, Fig. 8.8.

When goods are issued direct from stores, the requisition should confirm their issue; the only other action needed is for accounts to make a parallel entry for actual expenditure. A similar procedure can be carried out for *expenses*, but because of the nature of the information required for tax purposes, a different form is necessary.

For goods purchased, it is the practice in some organisations for the purchasing office to circulate copies of the order. If the required information has been entered on the purchase requisition this is not really necessary. If, however, the order is being placed against a Government contract, special conditions may apply (see Chapter 10). It should be a project office responsibility to ascertain that these have been stated correctly in accordance with the main contract. Therefore, as a matter of routine, copies of all orders should be sent to the project office with the returned requisition. In all cases a price must be stated; if the supplier cannot quote a firm price he should be asked for a provisional price, otherwise a maximum price should be placed on the order so that financial provision can be made. This is particularly important for orders placed between divisions of a large organisation, as it is the only way indirect control can be maintained. On the receipt of the goods, the *goods inwards* department should issue a *goods received* note. As this is an advice to the originator of the order, a copy must go to the group leader, and if it is passed via the project office they can check it with the

DIRECT MATERIAL ANALYSIS

		ACTIVITY
		COST CODE

COMMITTED

Date	Requisition		Ex-penses	Bought out	Sub-contract	Inter-dept. orders	Weekly total	Cum.
	No.		£ s d	£ s d	£ s d	£ s d	£ s d	£ s d
B/F								
TOTAL (C/F)								

ACTUAL

Date	Requisition	Ex-penses	Bought out	Sub-contract	Inter-dept. orders	Weekly total	Cum total
	No.	£ s d	£ s d	£ s d	£ s d	£ s d	£ s d
B/F							
TOTAL							

Fig. 8.8. Direct material analysis

purchase requisition and notate the progress record if necessary; this form should also be retained by the project office in the activity file.

When the *invoice* is received from the supplier, it should be passed to the project office for clearance, that is, for certification that the goods were as ordered, were acceptable, and that the value stated is correct and as provisioned. If the invoiced amount exceeds the maximum price then special action must be taken either by denying liability or by taking action through the research manager for an increase in approved expenditure. This procedure can also hold in the event of there being no goods received note, for example, where the order is for services. It can be useful for auditing purposes if the project office retains a copy of the invoice in the activity file, but this is not really necessary if the accounts filing system permits easy access. On receipt of the certified invoice the accounts can enter the actual expenditure, while proceeding with their normal accounting routine.

STATUS OF WORK

There are thus two records of the expenditure incurred on each activity of a project, derived from the same basic information; the accounts record, showing both actual and committed expenditure, and the project office *progress record* which gives in close proximity and in the same format both the estimated and committed expenditure. To complete the progress record, the status of the activity should be entered by the project leader, who each week should initial the space showing whether the activity is ahead, on, or behind schedule. It is convenient if the project office also marks in another colour the general status of expenditure thus making it easy for the research manager to observe any deviations. For convenience, the form illustrated (Fig. 6.4) has been based on the Kalamazoo system, so that, in the binder, only the 'status' is exposed. Other paperwork systems can be used, and the procedure described lends itself to computor operation, when only deviations from the plan of work need be printed out.

DEVIATION FROM PLAN

It is to be expected that deviations from the plan of work will arise when one, or a combination of two or more, of the control decisions at the beginning of this chapter are taken. (Assisting the project leader will obviously not require any routine paperwork.) Any revision of expenditure, aims or specification will involve a change in the authorised plan of work, and there must be a routine for recording the reason for the change and forecasting what may occur if the possible decisions are put into effect.

The estimate and progress record, Fig. 6.4, has been designed to permit the continuous up-dating of requirements. Immediately there is any deviation, the project leader, in conjunction with the research manager, should amend the record, following exactly the same procedure as with the original estimate, and assuming that there will be no change in either aims or specification. The amended estimate, whether consisting of a decrease or an increase in expenditure, can then be summarised on the front of an *amendment to project costs* form, Fig. 8.9. If the revised plan affects the expenditure of other activities either in amount, rate, or period of expenditure, these also must be entered, but unaffected activities can be omitted. It should be noted that this information will be complementary to the amended PERT chart when produced, and the procedure followed gives the basic information for revising the chart.

The reverse of the form should be used to indicate the changes in aims and/or specification that will be necessary if the plan of expenditure is unchanged. The possible effects of such changes in other areas of work must also be forecast.

The research manager can then make his recommendation, which might be a compromise solution. If the request is for an increase in expenditure within the reserve contingency, and no other activities are affected, then the project leader should be authorised to proceed and no further action will be necessary. In all other cases, however, special sanction may be required, since the decision to be taken may involve reallocation of resources, re-submission to the Board for increased finance, or even re-evaluation of the whole project with possible cut-off. As the manager's decision will involve a change in the plan of work previously authorised, a revised project order, or an amendment should be issued, which will in turn give rise to changes in the activity instruction cards.

When a *check point* has been noted on an activity estimate and progress record, the above procedure should be followed irrespective of whether there has been any deviation from the plan, since at this stage the activity and the possible alternatives must be reviewed critically.

If two or more activities show deviations concurrently, then if they are dependent all amendments must necessarily be shown on the same form to show the interrelationships. If, however, they are independent, separate forms can be used.

EXPECTED ACHIEVEMENT FACTOR

At the beginning of this chapter, in the section on concept of control, an expected achievement factor was introduced. As the idea of this factor is novel, it has not been utilised in the procedure described; however, its assessment can be of value in the decision making process, and therefore space can be allowed for this factor on the amendment to project costs form (Fig. 8.9). The probabilities of incurring a certain expenditure, and of achieving success, should be discussed by the R & D manager, the project leader, and staff; then, if a cut-off decision is involved, it

Note: If costs are not derived directly
from activity estimate, identify and
detail changes on reverse.

AMENDMENT TO ESTIMA

Task No.	Activity No.	Description and Remarks	Cost Heading	Actual Expenditure To Date	Quar
			Total		
			Total		
			Total		
			Total		
			Total		
			Grand Totals		
RS No.		Project			Custom

Fig. 8.9. Standard form for amendm

JECT COSTS (direct labour, materials and overheads)						Issue No.		
						Revised		
				Estimates				
arter	Quarter	Quarter	Half Year	Half Year	Year	Year	Year	Total
					Project No.		Sheet No.	
							Of	

stimated project costs

SPECIMEN COST RECORDS

Job Cost Record Sheet — 1

Factory .... Group .... Division .... C.D. Order No. 1

Customer	Deliver to:	Description:		Contract Value £	Prog. Pay't Limit £	'D' Order Limit £		Contract Value £	Prog. Pay't Limit £	'D' Order Limit £
Contract No.			Date				Date			
W. Order No.	Invoice to:									
D. Order No.										
Date Ack'd		Progress	% of Costs							

Year	Costs			Profit			Balance of Cover	Billed						Not Yet Billed						Memorandum		
	£	s.	d.	£	s.	d.	£	Invoice Date	Number	Costs £	s.	d.	Profit £	s.	d.	Costs £	s.	d.	Profit £	s.	d.	Retention £	Remarks
Month																						

Job Cost Record Sheet — 2

COST SUMMARY

C.D. Order No. 2

Year	Material			Labour				Overheads			Labour & Overhead Adjustment			Total			Remarks
	£	s.	d.	Hours	£	s.	d.	£	s.	d.	£	s.	d.	£	s.	d.	
Month	Sheet																

CHARGES—OWN DIVISION   C.D. Order No............   3

Job Cost Record Sheet

Year	D/Note I.F.A. No. Etc.	Amount		Hours Worked								Material		Labour		Overhead		Labour & Overhead Adjustment		Total	
				Dept.																	
		£	s.d.	1	2	3	4	Total	4	Total	4	Total									
													£	s.d.	£	s.d.	£	s.d.	£	s.d.	£	s.d.
W/Ending																				Grand Total	

PURCHASES AND EXPENSES INFEED DEVELOPMENT DEPARTMENTS   C.D. Order No............   4

Job Cost Record Sheet

Year	D/Note I.F.A. No. Etc.	Amount		Hours Worked								Material		Labour		Overhead		Labour & Overhead Adjustment		Total	
				Dept.																	
		£	s.d.	1	2	3	4	Total	4	Total	4	Total									
													£	s.d.	£	s.d.	£	s.d.	£	s.d.	£	s.d.
Month																				Grand Total	

PURCHASES AND EXPENSES INFEED PRODUCTION DEPARTMENTS   C.D. Order No............   5

Job Cost Record Sheet

Year	D/Note I.F.A. No. Etc.	Amount		Hours Worked	Material		Labour		Overhead		Labour & Overhead Adjustment		Total	
		£	s.d.											
					£	s.d.	£	s.d.	£	s.d.	£	s.d.	£	s.d.
Month													Grand Total	

Fig. 8.10. Specimen cost records. From The Management Accountant's Influence on Research and Development, SOUTHALL, H. P., Institute of Cost and Works Accountants, Summer School (1961). Reproduced by courtesy of the author and the Institute of Costs and Works Accountants

(continued overleaf)

Job Cost Record Sheet   OUTSIDE PURCHASES   C.D./ / Order No.   6

| Orders Placed | | | | | | | Year | Invoices | | | | Outstanding Commitment | | |
| Purchase Order | | Supplier | P.O. Item | Description | Amount | | | Item No. | Month | G.R.N. No. | Amount | | | Item No. | | | |
No.	Date				£	s.	d.				£	s.	d.		£	s.	d.

Job Cost Record Sheet   CASH PAYMENTS   C.D./ / Order No.   7

| Year | Voucher No. | Detail | Amount | | | Year | Month | Voucher No. | Detail | Amount | | |
Month			£	s.	d.					£	s.	d.

Fig. 8.10. (continued)

will stem from information supplied by those actually doing the work, but obtained in such a manner that, insofar as possible, it is unprejudiced.

FINANCIAL REPORTS

The prime purpose of financial control, is to report and measure the overall cost of a research establishment by means of a comparison statement between the actual expenditure and that budgeted for each accountancy period. Such a statement is a measure of past achievement and a guide to future action: this may entail controlling the intake or replacement of personnel, by examining the need for material or purchase indents, or by directive where necessary to eliminate waste and extravagance. In consequence the financial reports should reflect all phases of the research activity, that is, the programme, the manpower budget, the income and expenditure budget and the capital budget. It is essential, therefore, to maintain and report accurate costs of each project.

The preparation of the financial reports will involve summarising the costs shown on the labour and material analysis sheets. The *cost records* shown in Fig. 8.10 illustrate how this is done in a particular organisation.

It is the accountant's responsibility to ensure that bookings of costs and commitments are dealt with promptly; that cost records are as up to date as practicable; and that the *costing rates* are realistic and set to ensure that project costs are properly charged as the jobs proceed, and are not subject to late correction factors. In present day economic conditions, the costing rates, that is salaries and overheads, tend to escalate; if due allowance has not been made for this in the estimate, it is possible for the project to be overspent whilst still remaining within the estimated hours of work. For this reason the project leader should at suitable periods have a return of his committed expenditure. For comparing this return with the estimate, it is convenient to make a new issue of the estimated project costs, (Fig. 6.5) which can incorporate all amendments to the estimate. If any rates have been revised, the new rates should be used for preparing this estimate. If the authorised sums are exceeded, fresh sanction will have to be sought.

The R & D manager does not necessarily need the detailed information required by the project leader, but he will require a summary showing for each project the total labour, material, and overhead costs, both actual and committed, for each project; this should be presented in a form similar to that on which his budget was prepared. This information is often shown more conveniently in graph form. The same information will be required if the costs are to be invoiced.

As has been stated, financial control must extend both to overheads and capital purchases. Costs and commitments must be reported regularly, compared with budgets, and the position reappraised from time to time for control purposes. The impact of overspending on the capital account, and the effect, on other projects, must not be overlooked.

PROGRESS REPORTS

The purpose of recording each week the status of an activity is to indicate deviations from the plan. It is a function of the project leader to know the reasons for these deviations and to take correcting action. It is also necessary to keep management, customer, and other interested parties fully informed about what has been done and what it is proposed to do, both verbally and by written reports.

Most organisations call for a general *progress meeting* at monthly intervals, the agenda for which is usually prepared on **the** following basis:

(a) Brief details of technical achievements
(b) Variance from the plan of work, and expenditure
(c) Financial reports and revised estimates
(d) Work for next period.

There will naturally be discussion on all points raised and the mark of a good chairman is the manner in which he can limit the discussion to essentials. Proper minutes of the meetings must be kept and approved, to provide a record of decisions, and the reasons they were made, or not made.

In addition to the project meeting a *formal report* is often required. The preparation of these reports can be very time consuming, so they are usually prepared at either three- or six-monthly intervals. Their prime purpose is to inform senior management, who will not normally attend project meetings, of what has been done and what is proposed for the future. These reports are usually required in conjunction with the financial reports; taken together, they should indicate whether or not the project is being controlled effectively. The reports will also be required for the *project review*, but this must not be confused with control as the reports will be produced too late for this purpose.

The report will also provide a detailed historical record; for this aspect, the record of failures is as important as that of achievements, to prevent future workers from wasting time following unprofitable courses of action. The reports should also provide the basis for technical articles.

CONCLUSION

The principles of project and financial control of R & D have been described, together with a system that is illustrative of the best practice. It may be argued that the degree of control given by such a system is too great, or even unnecessary; but all concerned in R & D must understand that the good discipline involved, which is essential if the work is done on contract, can only contribute towards the success of a project and cannot detract from it.

It is unfortunate that the control of R & D is often thwarted by personalities at all levels. Research workers are notoriously optimistic, and as the solution is just round the corner the request for detailed analysis and information is often considered a waste of valuable time. The possible answer to this is for the control function to be exercised by computer, which might be programmed to take into account personalities as well as other variables.

REFERENCES

1. ACKOFF, R. L., *Scientific Method: Optimising Applied Research Decisions*, John Wiley Inc., NY (1962)
2. ACKOFF, R. L., *Structural Conflicts Within Organisations*, Unpublished paper, University of Pennsylvania (1964)
3. MARCHAK, T. A., 'Models, rules of thumb and development decisions', Chapter 11, *Operations Research in Research and Development*, Ed. Dean, B. V., John Wiley Inc., NY (1963)
4. SOUTHALL, H. P., *The Management Accountant's Influence on Research and Development*, Institute of Cost and Works Accountants, Summer School (1961)

BIBLIOGRAPHY

TENNANT, H. M., 'Costing for research and development', *Cost Accountant*, **36**, No. 5, p. 194, (1957)
DOD/NASA PERT/COST Guide, U.S. Government Printing Office, June (1962) Draft Supplement No. 1 (1963)
PERT/COST System Description Manual, United States Air Force, March (1963)
MOOTY, F. T., *An Introduction to PERT/COST*, U.S. Defence Documentation Centre, March (1964)
MCNEIL, J. F., 'Program control systems', *IEEE Trans. Engng. Mgmt.*, **EM-11**, No. 1, p. 29 (1965)
SURAN, J. J., 'R & D management: an operational view', *IEEE Trans. Engng. Mgmt.*, **EM-12**, No. 1, p. 14 (1965)
WALKER, J. D., HOWRY, E., 'A comparison of actual and allocated costs for work accomplished using NASA PERT', *IEEE Trans. Engng. Mgmt.*, **EM-12**, No. 3, p. 93 (1965)
BROOKS, H. B., 'Efficiency of complex projects', *IEEE Trans. Engng. Mgmt.*, **EM-13**, No. 3, p. 128 (1966)
SOISTMAN, E. C., 'Research and development can be controlled', *Res. Mgmt.*, **9**, No. 1, p. 15 (1966)

Chapter 9

The Legal Protection of Inventions

This chapter describes how inventions are protected legally by *patents*, *registered designs* or *copyright*, depending on the nature of the invention. *Trade marks* are also mentioned. Because of the complexity of patent law both in the United Kingdom and in the United States, the only person qualified to advise is a *patent agent* or *patent attorney*, who is cognisant of all aspects of the procedure. His knowledge and experience, however, can only lead to a successful application if he has the co-operation of the R & D manager, who must therefore be aware of the basic legal requirements so that he may conform to them.

PATENTS

HISTORY

The granting of monopolies was used by several sovereigns as a revenue raising scheme, but this, as history shows, was subject to many malpractices. In consequence such grants were abolished by Elizabeth I in 1601. Revived for a period by James I, they were finally declared illegal in 1624, when the Statute of Monopolies was passed. This statute declared that all monopolies would henceforth be void and of no legal effect. One proviso was, however, introduced; namely, that monopolies could be granted for a limited term in respect of 'the sole working or making of any manner of new manufacture within this realm, to the true and first inventor and inventors of such manufactures, which others at the time of making such letters patent and grants shall not use, so as also they be not contrary to the law or mischievous to the State, by raising prices of commodities at home, or hurt of trade, or generally inconvenient'.

The term 'patent' arose since it means 'open'; and the 'letters patent' were like the 'patent rolls', royal documents which, conferring titles of nobility, were delivered open, addressed to all the king's subjects.

The original statement quoted above is the basis for patent law in both the United Kingdom and the United States, where the first Congress at the second session in 1785 passed an act authorising a patent to be issued to the inventor of any useful act on his petition, 'granting to such petitioner, his heirs, administrators, or assigns for any term not exceeding fourteen years* the sole and exclusive right and liberty of making, using, and vending to others to be used, the said invention or discovery'.

LEGISLATION

Modern legislation dealing with the grant of patents is governed in the United Kingdom by the Patent Act (1949), (1957), (1961), the working procedure being given in the Patent Rules (1958) and the Patents (Amendments) Rules (1958), (1961), (1962). Similarly, in the United States, the Statutes are given in the United States Code, Title 35, the latest codification being Section 271, Public Law 593 (1952), which also includes the Rules of Practice (edition of June, 1960).

In British law the term *invention* is defined as 'any means of new manufacture the subject of letters patent and grant of privilege within Section 6 of the Statute of Monopolies and any new method of process or testing applicable to the improvement or control of manufacture, and includes an alleged invention'. In the United States there is no such statutory definition but the Courts have determined what cannot be considered an invention, for example, the exercise of ordinary engineering skill, substitution of materials, enlargement or changes in form, unification or multiplication of parts, unless new principles or new functions are involved; these negative rules, however, may be overruled by evidence of 'commercial success', when this has not been achieved previously.

In both countries the invention itself must conform to certain conditions before the grant of a patent is considered. These are:

(a) The invention must be tangible. An abstract idea cannot be patented, only the process or means by which the idea can be effected

(b) The invention must be useful. Although a high degree of utility is not called for, the proviso excludes anything frivolous

(c) The invention must display originality of thought, and must make a disclosure that is both new and novel. Under United Kingdom laws this precludes the disclosure of the invention by the inventor or any other person before the date of the application, otherwise the application may be invalidated. In principle the United States law is the same, with the exception that an inventor may disclose his invention and subsequently make an application provided that the time interval is not more than twelve months, and the invention has not been put to public use or sold.

*Legislation has extended this to seventeen years.

When the same invention is to be patented in both the United Kingdom and the United States, there should be no divergence of opinion between the Patent Examiners of either country in regard to (a) and (b); but to conform to (c), an American inventor must not disclose his invention before *filing* his complete *specification* in the United States, and a British inventor, if he has filed a preliminary specification, must not extend the date of filing his complete specification beyond twelve months from the date of his first application.

From the initial conception, a patent was not considered to be simply a legal method for the protection of an invention granted upon payment of fees, but it involved the patentee in a number of conditions, the chief of these under both United Kingdom and United States laws being:

(a) A proper definition of the scope of the invention is made public, that is the claims made for the invention are stated precisely

(b) The invention is fully disclosed, so that anyone can make use of it when the monopoly expires

(c) In the United Kingdom an invention must also be worked to the public interest, but an American patentee is neither bound to use his discovery himself, nor permit others to use it.

The application for a patent may be made by anyone who claims to be 'the true and first inventor', or, since the grant of a patent is considered to be a capital asset, by the inventor's heir, executor or administrator. In the United Kingdom an assignee may also apply, otherwise only a patent agent, or in some cases a solicitor, may apply for a patent on behalf of the inventor or assignee. In the United States the person who made the invention, unless he is dead or declared incapable of managing his own affairs, must make the application irrespective of whether the patent will be issued to him or his assignee; from this it follows that a company or organisation cannot of itself make an invention or make an application, although it may obtain ownership by purchase or otherwise.

When two or more persons are responsible for the invention, the names of all the persons involved must be mentioned in the application documents, must agree to the application, and for a United States patent must sign them. A person who has worked on the invention, but has not contributed to its essentials, cannot be expected to be considered a joint inventor.

It is customary for employees on first taking up their employment, to sign a document *assigning* the *rights* of any inventions they may make during the course of their employment to their employer, otherwise the assignee will be some person, company, corporation or organisation, that in return for some consideration has obtained all rights in the invention from the inventor. In the United States, should the inventor refuse to sign the application documents after assigning the invention, the assignee can apply to the Court for permission to make the application.

142

PROCEDURE IN THE UNITED KINGDOM

The *application* for the *patent rights* of an invention submitted for the first time in the United Kingdom may be made in either of two ways:*

(a) The applicant may apply for a patent enclosing a *provisional specification*. This application establishes the date on which the invention was made, and gives the applicant a period of twelve months (or fifteen, if an extension is applied for) to complete his invention, by which time a complete specification must be filed

(b) The applicant may omit the provisional specification and file the complete specification with his application.

The provisional specification must describe the invention and if possible give the basic principles on which it rests. Different embodiments, i.e. modifications allowing alternative usages, should be included as far as known or envisaged. The complete specification must give full details, including drawings, and must also include the applicant's claims as to which features are novel and for which he specifically needs protection from potential competitors. Owing to possible legal and other implications it is preferable that the layout and wording of specifications conform to the pattern that has been established by usage, and essential that the wording of the claims should allow the widest interpretation.

Immediately the application is made, the applicant is free to make his invention public by, for example, putting it to use, or publishing details. This, however, may result in another person working the invention, and in such an event the inventor has no redress until such time as the patent may be granted, and even then damages will only be awarded as from the date of publication of the complete specification.

When the complete specification has been lodged at the Patent Office, an examiner, after ensuring that the papers are in order, investigates the files of previous specifications, and also any other literature considered relevant, such as technical journals, proceedings of learned societies, and text books, in order to ensure that the claims for novelty are justified.

An *objection* to the grant of a patent may be made by any person within three months of the date of publication. The grounds for objection are laid down in the Act, and include:

(a) That the applicant obtained the invention from the objector, who was in fact the true and first inventor

(b) That there is a claim, of earlier date, to the invention, in another complete specification

(c) That the invention was published in a document available in this country before the date of application

(d) That the invention is not sufficiently described in the complete specification

*For detailed instructions of the requisite procedure, potential applicants are referred to the official pamphlets published free of charge by H.M. Patent Office, Chancery Lane, London, W.C.2.

(e) That the claims made in the specification with regard to the advantages, utility, and novelty of the invention are not true, or that the invention is obvious.

PROCEDURE IN THE UNITED STATES

Due to the common origin of both United Kingdom and United States patents, it might be expected that procedures would be similar in principle, but this is not the case. In the United States there is no procedure for filing a preliminary specification in order to establish the date at law on which the invention was made, and the full specification must be submitted with the application. There is, however, a twelve months' period of grace which is granted in certain circumstances.

For an invention submitted for the first time in the United States, the complete specification, including drawings and claims, preferably laid out in the manner described in Rule 77, must be submitted to the Commissioner of Patents, Washington 25, D.C., together with:

(a) A petition
(b) A power of attorney (if a patent attorney is employed)
(c) An oath administered by a duly authorised officer, e.g. a notary public, in accordance with Rule 66
(d) A filing fee
(e) Any assignment of the patent, which must also be acknowledged before a notary public.

Provided the documents are in order, a receipt will be forwarded to the applicant. This will indicate the Patent Office examiner responsible for determining whether the specification and drawings are capable of producing the intended result, and whether the application is new and novel; that is, it does not repeat any matter disclosed or claimed in previously granted patents either in the United States or abroad, or in the literature, or that the invention has not been in public use or sale, with the proviso that the applicant has a twelve months period of grace between making a disclosure and making his application. In these circumstances he may be asked to prove the date of the actual reduction to practice of his invention.

Should the examiner reject the application, he will detail his reasons; within a period of six months (in some cases the Patent Office may request a reply within a shorter period) the applicant may appeal, amend his specification or claims, or make a disclaimer. The form of amendments and disclaimers are governed by the rules, and it should be noted that, as in the United Kingdom, no new material can be added.

When all requirements are met and in consequence the examiner considers that the invention is patentable, he makes an *interference search* to determine whether there are any pending applications for essentially the same invention. An interference is defined as a 'proceeding initiated for the purpose of determining the question of priority of invention between two or more parties claiming substantially the same patentable invention'. For determining priority, the significant date is when the actual reduction to practice of the invention took place, although the date of conception and the diligence with which the invention was reduced to practice may also be taken into account. If the examiner finds a co-pending application, the junior applicant, that is the applicant with the latest filing date, will be asked to 'state under oath the date and character of the earliest fact or act, susceptible of proof, which can establish the date of conception of the invention'. If this date is before the filing date of the first applicant, an interference will be declared and the applications will be sent to the Examiners of Interference. It is beyond the scope of this book to discuss the procedure that will then arise, but the reader is referred to the specialist books listed in the bibliography.

It will be seen from the above that third parties can only object to the grant of patents when they have been notified by the Patents Office that they are parties to an interference. However, after a patent is granted, and should the patentee sue for infringement, the defendent may seek to prove that the patent is invalid on broadly similar grounds to those laid down for objecting to United Kingdom patents, with the addition of 'the invention has been abandoned to the public before the application was filed'.

RIGHTS OF THE PATENTEE

A patent is a *capital asset* and the owner may not only grant licences, but also sell, mortgage, or bequeath it as he wishes. In the United Kingdom, if he does anything in 'restraint of trade', such as attaching condition to the grant of a licence which will unfairly prejudice industry, or abuses his monopoly rights by not exploiting the patent, then, after three years from the date of sealing, at the request of any interested party, the Comptroller may compel him to grant licences, or may even revoke the patent. Similar restrictions apply in the United States, although there, the owner of the patent has more freedom of action.

In neither country does the State assume responsibility for enforcement of a patent; for any infringement, the onus is on the patentee to establish the validity of his complaints by taking legal action. As infringement can only occur after the patent has been granted, in the United Kingdom damages can only be obtained for use subsequent to the date of sealing. In the United States, however, the total profit made may be taken into account in assessing damages.

RECORDS OF INVENTIONS

In view of the possibility of interference proceedings in the United States, it is essential that acceptable records of an invention are kept to prove the date of conception, the date of actual reduction to practice, and diligence in reducing to practice. Such records are particularly important if any information concerning an invention is made public; without such records an interloper may file a prior application and by 'swearing back of the publication date' obtain a valid patent.

Records acceptable by the courts can naturally take a number of forms, but preferably they should be written in ink in a bound book with numbered pages. *Laboratory notes* are acceptable records, provided they are supplemented as necessary to give an adequate description of the invention and the work done. Each page and insert should be signed and dated by the inventor and the book should be shown periodically to technically competent witnesses, who must sign and date the book stating that they have a full understanding of the work and confirming the results of any demonstrations.

Many firms, particularly when they have a patents department, try to simplify this procedure by means of a *patent disclosure sheet*, a good example of which is shown in Fig. 9.1. In government contracts, (see Chapter 10 with regard to contract provisions for patents), the United States Departments and Agencies have their own disclosure forms which must be completed by the contractor. Such disclosure sheets have the added advantage of providing a routine method for the research worker to submit ideas to the patent department, who will advise as to whether the idea is patentable.

Although records of the above nature are not usual in the United Kingdom, and furthermore it is doubtful whether they would be acceptable at law, a procedure such as the patents disclosure sheet in modified form could be advantageous, particularly if a patent application was objected to on the grounds that the applicant was not the 'true and first inventor'.

INTERNATIONAL PROTECTION

Fifty-four countries, including the United Kingdom and the United States, are members of the Paris Union Convention for the protection of industrial property. Countries that remain outside the Convention are the U.S.S.R.,* the South American Republics with the exception of Brazil and Ecuador, and most Asian countries.

The most important provisions of this international convention are:

(a) There is no discrimination in a country's patent laws between its own nationals and those of a convention country. For example, a British national is entitled to seventeen years protection from the date of the grant of his patent in the United States, although his United Kingdom patent has only a term of sixteen years from the date of filing the complete specification. Furthermore a foreigner does not need to have a residence in the country where the patent is sought

*During 1965 the Soviet Union stated that it was prepared to join the Paris Convention.

FORM PAT. 3009 7-65

RCA **PATENT DISCLOSURE DATA SHEET**

	For Patent Operations Use Only (For Acknowledgment and Atty. Assignment)
(Date Received)	RCA Docket No. _____
	Date: _____
	Domestic Patents Mgr. _____
	Patent Attorney: _____
	Origin: _____

To: Patent Operations
Radio Corporation of America
David Sarnoff Research Center
Princeton, New Jersey 08540

The herein described invention is submitted
pursuant to my employment agreement.

1. Date of this disclosure: _____
2. DESCRIPTIVE TITLE: _____
3. PURPOSE, SUMMARY AND PROBABLE USES: _____

Answer All Questions — Use N/A when Not Applicable — Submit Original — Keep Copy for Your Files

4. Attached hereto is "Detailed Description" comprising Form Pat. 3010 ( ) pages and the following papers, prints, samples, etc. _____
5. Invention described _____, 19___, in Engineering Notebook No. _____ Pages _____
6. Device constructed on _____, 19___. 7. Shop Order # _____
8. Tested on _____, 19___. 9. Test Witnessed by _____
  Bldg _____ Flr. _____ City and State _____ RCA Tel. Ext. _____
10. State any plans for use of the invention _____
11. If this invention has been described in any publication or report, identify: _____
12. Was invention *either* (a) conceived or (b) *first* actually reduced to practice in the course of or under Government Contract(s) or Subcontract(s)? (a) Yes _____ No _____ If "Yes," give date: _____, 19___
  (b) Yes _____ No _____ If "Yes," give date: _____, 19___. **(See explanation on reverse side)**
13. If answer either to 12(a) or 12(b) is "Yes" list contract(s) or subcontract(s) numbers:
  (a) _____ (b) _____
14. Is the invention embodied in any material either (a) furnished or (b) to be furnished under Government Contract(s) or Subcontract(s) ? (a) Yes _____ No _____ (b) Yes _____ No _____
15. If answer either to 14(a) or 14(b) is "Yes" list contract(s) or subcontract(s) numbers:
  (a) _____ (b) _____
16. Security classification of the Invention _____
(If any part of this disclosure is classified, the **disclosure should be appropriately stamped and transmitted under security procedures.**)

17. (1) Full Name _____ Citizen of _____
  First   Middle   Last

T Home Address _____
Y   Street   City   County   State
P RCA Div. or Subsidiary _____ Bldg. No. _____ Flr. _____ City & State _____ RCA Tel. Ext. _____
E Occupation No. _____ Occupation Title _____
or (2) Full Name _____ Citizen of _____
P   First   Middle   Last
R Home Address _____
I   Street   City   County   State
N RCA Div. or Subsidiary _____ Bldg. No. _____ Flr. _____ City & State _____ RCA Tel. Ext. _____
T Occupation No. _____ Occupation Title _____

18. Sign full name(s) (1) _____ (2) _____

SPACE BELOW RESERVED FOR WITNESS
(An effort should be made to obtain the signature of the person to whom the inventor(s) first disclosed the invention)

19. The invention was first explained to me by the above identified inventor(s) on _____, 19___, and is understood by me.

Signature of Witness _____ Date of Signature _____, 19___

Name of Witness (Type or print) _____

RCA Location: City & State _____ Bldg. _____ Flr. _____ Tel. Ext. _____

Fig. 9.1. Patent disclosure sheet. Courtesy: Radio Corporation of America

(b) An applicant for a patent, after making his first application in a convention country, has in the other countries a right of priority for a period of twelve months, that is he may disclose the substance of the patent during this period without prejudicing the grant of his patent. An applicant who wishes to claim priority is required to make a declaration indicating the date of filing and the country of the first application. The convention also provides that the specification and drawings of the first application, which are known as the priority documents, do not require authentication and may be filed within three months of the application. A result of this provision is that the applicant can investigate the market before incurring the trouble and expense of making an application in other countries

(c) The domestic laws of a convention country protect any patentable inventions displayed at official or officially recognised international exhibitions.

Subject to these provisions, the procedure for applying for a patent in either the United Kingdom or United States is as described previously, except that the declaration required by the United States can be made before a United States diplomatic or consular official. Due to the length of time that elapses between the application for a patent and its grant, it is possible for the second application to be granted before the first; if one patent is granted, it need not necessarily mean that the second will be granted, as each is considered according to the domestic laws of the country.

In certain British territories and countries of the Commonwealth, United Kingdom Patents are either automatically protected, can be registered, or patents granted on application after the grant of the United Kingdom patent.

In Scandinavia a patent may be obtained valid in Denmark, Norway, Sweden and Finland by filing the application in any one of the countries. A similar procedure is under consideration for the Common Market countries, that is: Belgium, the Netherlands, France, West Germany, Italy and Luxembourg.

With the growth of trade with the U.S.S.R., protection there may be of importance. Since Russia is not a convention country no priority is given and the patent application must be made simultaneously with the first application, since the publication of any information elsewhere, including the publication of the first patent, will invalidate the application.

DESIGNS

It is possible for a patent to be granted for some comparatively minor modification to an existing invention, provided the specification makes it clear that the claim as to which features are novel rests entirely on this modification. In the case of an invention which is simple, *registration* of the *design* in the United Kingdom or a *design patent* in the United States is sometimes considered; but in principle this cannot be done if the design, that is the shape or configuration, is dictated solely by the function of the invention and not primarily to appeal to the eye. This excludes methods of construction, and it is improbable that the design of an electronic component, or the layout of a circuit would be acceptable. To be acceptable, a design must be new, original, ornamental, and be intended to be manufactured in quantity, otherwise the principles of copyright may apply.

It must be stressed that in the United Kingdom a registered design must never be thought of as a patent, although in the legislation many of the principles of patent law apply; the legislation is given in the Registered Designs Act 1949, the Designs Rules 1949, and the Designs (Amendment) Rules 1955 and 1961. Registration normally exists for a period of five years from the date of registration, but can be extended for two further periods, each of five years. Like a patent, a registered design is a capital asset, and may be assigned and licensed.

In the United States, patents for designs are covered by the same Statute as patents, with two amendments; first, the period of grace is only six months, not twelve as for a normal patent; second, the patent is not granted for seventeen years but only for a period of three and a half, seven or fourteen years; the applicant must specify which period in his application.

COPYRIGHT

To be patentable an invention must be capable of being manufactured. Abstract invention, for example a mathematical analysis or theory, can only be protected by copyright, although there is no copyright in a basic idea, but only in the means by which that idea is formulated.

By copyright is meant the exclusive right of ownership of an author or artist for any original work, such as an article, book, photograph, technical drawing, or model. This right extends to printing, reprinting, revising, translating or presenting in any manner to the public. Copyright is a capital asset which may be disposed of by the author or any subsequent owner as he wishes, there being no statutory limitations either in the United Kingdom or United States.

In the United Kingdom the conditions for copyright are given in the Copyright Act 1956. There is no necessity to claim or register, the copyright coming into existence the moment the work is created and lasting for the lifetime of the author and for fifty years after his death. Whether or not the work is published, that is copies are issued to the public, is not relevant, nor is the period of existence changed by change of ownership.

For unpublished work in the United States copyright is protected under Common Law, but on publication the Common Law protection is lost, and to secure the right of ownership the statutory requirements of the Copyright Law given in United States Code Title 17, 1963 must be met. This states that the publication must contain a notice on the title page, or page immediately following, consisting of the word 'Copyright', the abbreviation 'Copr.', or the symbol '©', accompanied by the name of the copyright proprietor, and the year in which copyright was first secured by publication. The claim must also be registered and for this purpose works are grouped into thirteen classes. Those relevant to the scope of this book are:

(a) Books, including composite and cyclopedic works, directories and other compilations
(b) Periodicals, including newspapers
(c) Lectures, addresses. (This includes works that will not be published)
(d) Drawings or plastics works of a scientific or technical character
(e) Photographs
(f) Prints and pictorial illustrations including prints or labels used for articles of merchandise
(g) Motion pictures other than photoplays.

Registration is made on the appropriate form for the class, which should be sent to the Copyright Office, Library of Congress, Washington, D.C., accompanied by a fee. Registration lasts for a period of twenty-eight years, but in the twenty-seventh year renewal can be sought for a further period of twenty-eight years.* The application can be made by the author or proprietor of the copyright, including executors, administrators, or assignees, and if ownership changes at any time this may also be recorded. Finally, following publication, two copies of the work must be deposited in the Copyright Office, together with an affidavit that certain printing requirements have been met.

Both the United Kingdom and the United States are signatories to the Universal Copyright Convention drawn up by UNESCO in 1952. Like the Paris Union Convention for patents, the main provision is that there is no discrimination between a country's own nationals and those of a convention country. Hence in the United Kingdom the proprietor of a United States copyright has no statutory requirements to observe, on the other hand a British publication must conform with the United States requirements, in that it must contain the statutory notice, one copy must be deposited with the Copyright Office, and registration made; in lieu, a catalogue card containing the information required by the regulations is acceptable.

When the work is produced in the course of an author's employment, the employer can have a right to the copyright. It is therefore essential to obtain an employer's *permission to publish* and it may be advisable to obtain a precise statement as to the employer's interest in the copyright, when work is commissioned by publishers, or accepted by a learned or professional society, since it is usually a condition that the copyright is transferred, to ensure that the paper is not made public elsewhere without permission.

*Congress is expected to make the period of registration the same as that for the U.K.

If the work provides the basis for a patentable invention, care must be taken to ensure that publication does not prejudice the subsequent grant of a patent, either by disclosing means by which the invention can be made, or by providing information which would enable another person to make the invention. If there is any doubt, publication should be postponed until after the patent application has been filed. The author may desire, however, to ensure that he will be considered as the originator of the work, and this may be established by getting the work dated in front of a Commissioner of Oaths, or Notary Public, accepted by a publisher or learned society for making public after a certain date, or other means by which the date of origin can be established legally. It should be noted that in the United States, a scientific or technical drawing can be registered even if it is part of a pending patent application, although it cannot be registered after the issue of a patent.

As with patents, the onus of establishing that a copyright is not infringed rests with the owner. In the United Kingdom the act states that copyright material may be used for certain purposes, such as research, criticism, provided there is sufficient acknowledgement, for example, a reference; the same principle is accepted in the United States. There is no copyright in a basic idea, but only in the means by which that idea is formulated; this includes paraphrasing, redrawn diagrams etc.

Government publications in the United States are normally in the public domain, that is, there is no copyright, but in the United Kingdom the copyright is retained by Her Majesty's Stationery Office (H.M.S.O.).

TRADEMARKS

In marketing an invention, consideration should be given to associating with it a *trade mark*. As the duration of registration of a trade mark can be extended indefinitely, its continuing use, after the expiry of a patent, may safeguard the goodwill created.

Registration of trademarks was first introduced in the United Kingdom in 1875, the first being the Bass Red Triangle. It is now governed by The Trade Marks Act 1938, the Trade Marks Rules 1938, and the Trade Marks (Amendment) Rules 1955. Registration, if accepted, gives the owner only limited rights in preventing its use by others. A trade mark that is unregistered can be established by usage. Both registered and unregistered trade marks are protected by common law. Registration, however, simplifies the legal position by establishing prior ownership and giving notification of intent to use.

To be acceptable for registration, a mark must be distinctive but not descriptive either pictorially or otherwise of the class of goods with which it is proposed to be used. In addition, it must not interfere with common rights in the use of everyday speech, or deceive the public. It should not include such words as patented, registered design etc. Preliminary advice as to whether a proposed mark may be accepted for registration is given by the registrar for a fee. There are thirty-four classes of goods for which marks can be registered (for example, electronic equipment is in Class 9), and it is possible for the same or a very similar mark to be registered in different classes by different manufacturers, when there is no likelihood of confusion between their products.

When an application has been accepted the mark is advertised in the *Trade Marks Journal*, and any person objecting must do so within one month. It is usual for the objector to contact the applicant before making the formal objection, in order to give him the opportunity of modifying or withdrawing the application.

If there is no objection or the objection is overruled, then on payment of the registration fee, the mark is entered in the Register. Initially, registration lasts for a period of seven years, and may be renewed for subsequent periods of fourteen years.

In the United States the requirements for a trade mark are broadly the same, but a mark cannot be registered unless it has been in use for about one year either in inter-state or inter-country trade. Provided the trade mark meets the regulations, registration consists of a petition, statement, drawings, five specimens, and oath sent to the Patent Office, together with a fee.

Trade marks are capital assets and may be assigned, licensed or transferred.

BIBLIOGRAPHY

PATENT LAW

United Kingdom
MEINHARDT, P., *Inventions, Patents and Monopoly*, Stevens & Sons, 2nd edit. (1950)
CARR, L. H. A., WOOD, J. C., *Patents for Engineers*, Chapman & Hall (1959)
*SHELLEY, K. E., *Terrell and Shelley on the Law of Patents*, Sweet & Maxwell, 10th edit. (1961)
*BLANCO WHITE, T. A., *Patents for Inventions and the Registration of Industrial Designs*, Stevens & Sons, 3rd edit. (1962)

United States
RHODES, F. H., *Elements of Patent Law*, Cornell Univ. Press, NY (1949)
*TOULMIN, H. A., *Handbook of Patents*, Van Nostrand Inc. (1949)
THOMAS, E., *Chemical Inventions and Chemical Patents*, Bender, Albany, NY (1950)
BERLE, A. K., DE CAMP, L. S., *Inventions and their Management*, Van Nostrand Inc., Scranton, 3rd edit. (1951)
WISE, J. K., *Patent Law in the Research Laboratory*, Reinhold Publishing Corp., NY (1955)
TUSKA, C. D., *Inventors and Inventions*, McGraw-Hill, NY (1957)
BRINK, R. E., GIPPLE, D. C., HUGHESDON, H., *An Outline of United States Patent Law*, Interscience Publishers Inc., NY (1959)
TUSKA, C. D., *An Introduction to Patents for Inventors and Engineers*, Dover Publications Inc., NY (1965)
*DELLER, A. W., *Walker on Patents*, Baker, Voorhis & Co., NY (1937) plus cumulative annual supplements

International
European Convention Relating to the Formalities Required for Patent Applications, Dec. 11th, 1953, H.M.S.O. (1955)
Soviet Patent and Trade Mark Law, Code 70-80, H.M.S.O. (1960)

SINGER, STERN, CARLBERG, *Foreign Patent and Trade Mark Requirements*, Chicago (1957)

Derwent Patents Manual 1964, Derwent Publications, London (1963)

SCHADE, H., *Patents at a Glance*, Carl Heymanns Verlag KG, Munich, English edit. (1964)

Patent and Trade Mark Review, Trade Activities Inc., NY, publ. monthly

Propriété Industrielle, Geneva Bureau of the Paris Union, English edit., publ. monthly

COPYRIGHT

United Kingdom
*EDDY, J. P., *The Law of Copyright*, Butterworth (1957)

United States
*STURGESS, A. G., *Patent and Copyright Protection*, Omaha (1951)

TRADE MARKS

United Kingdom
*FLETCHER MOULTON, H., LANGDON-DAVIES, P. G., *The Law of Merchandise Marks*, Butterworth (1957)

*Professional reference books

Chapter 10

Business Contracts

Throughout his career, the R & D worker, whether in a university, Government department or industry, will be associated with *contracts*. Even if not concerned in making a contract, he must be acquainted with the principles of *contract law* since he may, as an agent, be responsible for:

(a) Acting as negotiator
(b) Giving instructions to the contractor
(c) Accepting instructions on behalf of the contractor
(d) Approving work done
(e) Authorising payment
(f) Extending time of contract
(g) Acting as arbitrator.

The Law of Contract, both in the United Kingdom and the United States, is based on English Common Law and the principles are essentially the same, although the terminology differs in some aspects.

As Government departments are the major contractors for R & D, the special provisions that can apply to such contracts are discussed.

CONTRACTS

A contract is an *agreement* which is enforceable at law. Such an agreement takes place when two or more parties declare their consent, either verbally or in writing, regarding anything which they will or will not do. There are four elements that make up a contract:

(a) *Mutual agreement,* or *consent.* This is declared through the common intent to contract and the communication of an *offer*, which must be serious, clear and definite, followed by *acceptance* which is *express* if communicated, or *implied* if it can be inferred by acts. An offer may be revoked at any time before acceptance, and may lapse after a stated time, or reasonable time; it can only remain open for a specific time if some *consideration* is made, i.e. payment. If an offer and acceptance are communicated by post, the time of each is the time of posting. If an offer is rejected, it cannot be accepted subsequently, and the making of a counter offer cancels the original offer. If a mistake is made in the subject matter, e.g. specification, this is considered a *material mistake*; as there cannot be mutual agreement, the contract must be void

(b) *Capacity*. This means in law the ability of the persons to make a contract. Minors (those under 21 years), the insane or inebriated persons are not considered to have the capacity, and contracts they make may be *voidable*. A corporation can be bound by any person acting under its authority, express or implied, in matters of small importance and frequent occurrence, contracts arising in the ordinary course of its business, and those incidental to the purpose for which it was created; otherwise, it can only bind itself if the seal of the corporation is affixed to a written contract

(c) *Consideration*. A contract must involve an exchange of goods, money, or services; the consideration* is the thing of value which is exchanged. It involves both a benefit and detriment to both parties. When *promises* are exchanged the promises themselves are the consideration, and a *bilateral contract* is made. If a promise is made by one party, which is accepted by an act, the contract is *unilateral* and is only binding when the act is completed, that is, consideration made. (A promise can be made without consideration in a *deed*, when the promise is called a *covenant*; the deed itself is distinguished from a simple contract by being a writing, sealed and delivered by the person making it.)

The law does not generally inquire into the *adequacy* of the consideration. (A mistake in regard to the value of the consideration is considered *immaterial*, and the contract holds, although it may be re-negotiated)

(d) *Legality*. Where the consideration for the promise, or the promise itself is illegal the agreement is void. An illegal agreement may be contrary to:

1. Positive Law—A contract may be declared void if it contravenes an Act, or, in the United States, State Law; for example, qualified persons concerned in the pursuance of their profession in dealing with the public must be licensed. Also, in most States, contracts made on Sundays are illegal unless they involve the preservation of life or property. In neither country can wagers be recovered. Again, usury or the charging of excessive interest is illegal

2. Morality—e.g. a contract made under duress

3. Public policy—The most important restriction within this class is that concerning *restraint of trade*; such agreements are considered void if they limit competition or place restrictions on the exercise of a gainful trade or profession to an unreasonable extent, so as to constitute hardship. Another example that occurs today is trading with Communist Bloc countries.

---

*Consideration has no place in Scottish Law, and is not necessary in making a contract, in consequence a promise may be binding without consideration.

When a contract is illegal only in part, the part which is legal may be enforced if it can be separated from the part that is illegal. A party to an illegal agreement cannot recover money that has been paid.

A contract may be *terminated* by:

(a) *Performance*. When all parts of a contract are carried out as agreed the contract is *completely performed*. It may be considered to be *substantially performed* if the terms are carried out except for small or minor deviations. If *partially performed*, one or more important parts or duties remains to be completed. It should be noted that if the contract calls for 'personal satisfaction', the contract is not completely performed until the party is reasonably satisfied with the performance

(b) *Mutual agreement or rescission*

(c) *Breach*. A *breach of contract* arises if either or both parties do not perform their duties. If one party fails to perform, or the performance of the obligation of one party depends on the performance of the other party's obligation and this does not occur, the contract may be considered to be discharged; the aggrieved party then has the right to recover *damages* sufficient to compensate for such losses that he may have suffered. As a general rule an action for damages cannot be begun until the time has elapsed by when the contract should have been performed.* If, however, an *anticipatory breach* is made, that is, one party declares that he does not intend to perform, action can be begun immediately. It should be noted that if a contract is partially performed before a breach takes place, the other party may not be able to repudiate all liability under the contract

(d) *Impossibility of performance*. A party to a contract is not excused because of difficulties that may arise, although he may provide in the contract for certain eventualities. A contract, however, may be discharged in the event of the destruction of particular matter, or incapacity if personal services are called for. The death or bankruptcy of either party does not necessarily discharge a contract, since rights and liabilities pass to executors and trustees

(e) *Operation of law*. If changes in the law make a legal contract illegal, it is then considered to be discharged.

UNITED KINGDOM—THE SALE OF GOODS ACT

Contracts for the procurement of goods in the United Kingdom are governed by the Sale of Goods Act, 1893 (56 & 57 Vic., c. 31) together with conditions that may be laid down by both the seller and buyer.

The expression goods means all tangible movable property except

---

*In England and Wales the Statute of Limitations prevents an action being brought after six years of the cause of the action; in Scotland there are different periods of limitation.

money. If they are identified clearly when the contract is drawn up they are called *specific goods*, otherwise they are termed *future goods*.

A *sale* is made when the ownership of the goods is transferred; until this occurs the contract is called an *agreement to sell*.

Under the Act, a contract for the sale of goods of the value of £10 or upwards is not enforceable by action, unless one of the following can be proved:

(a) The buyer accepts part of the goods sold and actually receives the same. (In this context 'accepts', means the buyer shows acceptance of the contract by action or otherwise, and 'receives' means that the goods have been delivered to him, his agent, or according to the terms of the contract)

(b) The buyer gives something in earnest to bind the contract or in part payment

(c) There is a written contract, note, or memorandum, signed by the party to be charged, or his agent in that behalf.

A *condition* in a contract is a material term or *provision* of the contract, the failure to observe which by one party entitles the other to treat the contract as repudiated, frees him from his obligation under it, and usually gives him a right of action for breach of contract against the party in fault. These conditions often modify the contract of sale that would exist if the transaction was left solely to the provisions of the Sale of Goods Act. The implications of such conditions need legal advice, and are beyond the scope of this book, although those appertaining to Government contracts are discussed briefly below.

A *warranty*, such as might be given for the quality and fitness of the goods, is not considered a material term of a contract, but collateral to it. A breach of warranty by the seller does not entitle the buyer to reject or return the goods, but does give him a right to damages. A warranty can be express or implied.

UNITED KINGDOM—STANDARD CONDITIONS
OF GOVERNMENT CONTRACTS

To give uniformity of contract conditions between the principal Government purchasing departments and contractors, a booklet has been published, entitled *Standard Conditions of Government Contracts for Stores Purposes*, H.M.S.O., (1962). Tender and contract documents contain only a reference to the booklet numbers of the conditions applicable to the contract, together with any special conditions or amendments to the standard conditions.

The conditions given in Part I of the Booklet are normally used by all departments, whilst those in Part II are used as appropriate. Conditions that may be applied to an R & D contract are:

32A. *Patents*, etc., *royalty*, *licence fee*, or similar expense will not be allowed unless specifically agreed by the Authority.

43. *Price fixing*. For the purpose of fixing prices, the contractor shall, if the Authority so requires, permit the inspection of books, accounts, and other documents.
56. Break. This gives the Authority power to determine the Contract.
59. *Security measures*.

Special conditions not contained in the booklet that may be applicable to R & D contracts made by the Ministry of Technology are:

6/14. Ownership of patents and registered designs (January 1958). This assigns to the Government a licence for any patents arising from the contract
6/15(A). Design rights (A) (February 1958). This permits the Authority to make use of the design for official purposes
6/21. Drawings, specifications and manufacturing data (January 1958). The contractor must retain a complete set of drawings for not less than two years after completion of the contract, which the Authority may demand and use as it thinks fit
6/23. Special jigs, tools, etc., (July 1965). The scale must be approved by the Authority, the cost being included in the contract and the contractor must maintain a register. They must be kept in good order until the Authority gives disposal instructions
6/90. Copyright clause (November 1958). The contractor will ensure that copyright will be vested with him, and that no copyright work will be published without the consent in writing of the Authority.

Furthermore it is now becoming current practice to include an *International Collaboration Agreement* clause, which gives the Authority wider rights than normal, in order to promote any international collaboration agreement in existence or that may be made, e.g. the Concorde project.

It should be noted that all conditions given in a contract must also be applied to any sub-contract over the value of £2,500, for services or goods that are not proprietary.

UNITED STATES—THE STATUTE OF FRAUDS

In the United States there is no equivalent to the United Kingdom Sale of Goods Act, but the Statute of Frauds provides that certain types of agreement cannot be proved in court unless they are in writing and signed by the party to be bound. Of specific interest are:

(a) Contracts not to be performed within one year. It should be noted that if there is the slightest chance that a contract can be completed within one year, it need not be in writing
(b) Contracts for the sale of goods and merchandise over a specified sum of money. (In most States it is $500).

A memorandum can satisfy the statutory requirements if it affords complete written evidence of the entire agreement · and is properly signed. It may consist of a series of letters or other written documents. Exceptions to a written contract may be made, as in British law, if a buyer accepts and receives parts of the goods, or makes part payment.

Provisions of sale may also be applied by both seller and buyer; for the implications of such conditions, legal advice is necessary.

UNITED STATES—GOVERNMENT PURCHASING

The most important statutory bases for the conduct of *procurement* by the United States Federal Government are the Federal Property and Administrative Services Act of 1949 (41 U.S.C. 251 *et seq.*), and the former Armed Services Procurement Act of 1947 (now Chapter 137 of Title 10 of the United States Code). Under the authority of the former, the Federal Procurement Regulations System has been established, and this is followed by most civilian agencies. Military agencies are bound by both Acts, where the former does not conflict with the latter, and the Department of Defence has issued the Armed Services Procurement Regulation which establishes uniform policies and procedures.

As their titles imply, these acts and regulations deal with the procedure for procurement of contracts and detail standard provisions, accounting methods, management practices, the termination of contracts, etc.

In the Standard Provisions for Defence Contracts, an *audit clause* is usually included for all contracts over $100,000, which means that accurate accounts must be kept for a period of three years for possible examination and subsequent price adjustment. The accounting system must be approved except in the case of fixed price contracts. It should be noted that certain charges may or may not be allowable, and it is advisable to have advance agreement.

With reference to patents, data, and copyright generated during the performance of R & D contracts, the DOD concept is not to acquire more than a comprehensive licence, (free user) unless it is considered to be in the public interest to have full title.

PERT and PERT/COST information is now usually mandatory for DOD contracts.

BIBLIOGRAPHY

British Publications
ATIYAH, P. S., *An Introduction to the Law of Contracts*, Clarendon Press, Oxford (1961)
REAR, J., *The Law of Contracts*, Sweet and Maxwell (1963)
GUEST, A. G., *Anson's Law of Contract*, Clarendon Press, Oxford, 22nd edit. (1964)
HARDING BOULTON, A., *The Making of Business Contracts*, Sweet and Maxwell (1965)

American Publications
KAUFMAN, J. J., *Contracts Outline*, University Outline Publications, Illinois (1961)
WERBIN, J. V., *Law for Contractors, Architects and Engineers*, Central Book Company (1961)

R & D Administration

ABBETT, R. W., *Engineering Contracts and Specifications*, John Wiley Inc., NY, 4th edit. (1963)

BURBY, W. E., *Law Refresher: Contracts*, West, 3rd edit. (1963)

TRUEGER, P. M., *Accounting Guide for Defense Contracts*, Commerce Clearing House Inc., 4th edit., NY (1963)

CUPPOLA, A. J., KATZ, H., *The Law of Business Contracts*, John Wiley Inc., NY (1964)

FULLER, L. L., *Basic Contract Law*, West, (1964)

FONSECA, J. R., *Introduction to the Law of Contracts*, Addison-Wesley Pub. Co., Mass. (1965)

General

Government Purchasing in Europe, North America and Japan—Regulations and Procedures, O.E.C.D., Paris (1966)

Chapter 11

The Technical Library

The starting point for most new projects is a literature search, and the R & D manager must ensure that his staff know how to formulate their requirements and make efficient use of *library services*. Furthermore, if a technical library is under his direct command, he must have knowledge of its procedures and functions. This chapter covers the *classification of information, search procedures, sources of reference,* and *library organisation.*

CLASSIFICATION OF INFORMATION

The systems used to classify information are by no means self-explanatory; in the UK the most common is the *Universal Decimal Classification* (U.D.C.), which is recommended by the British Standards Institution, although it is considered by many libraries to be unwieldy and inefficient. This is derived from the *Dewey Decimal Classification*[1] which divides all knowledge into ten broad groups as follows:

0	General works, including reference
100	Philosophy
200	Religion
400	Languages
500	Science
600	Technology
700	Arts and recreations
800	Literature
900	Geography, biography and history

The notation, to which up to three decimal figures may be added, allows a considerable breakdown of each group into divisions and topics, for example, 621.384 denotes technology-engineering-mechanical-electrical-communications-radio. It should be noted that any sequence of figures is unique for every division and topic.

The U.D.C. uses a similar numbering system to the Dewey, but care must be taken to differentiate between the two, since, owing to the greater expansion of U.D.C., the numbers may not be identical. This greater expansion, together with multiple numbers, permits indexing and cataloguing in any of the relevant classifications. Table 11.1, gives those numbers that may be found most useful. There is no simple system by which the numbers can be derived, and for a full breakdown, reference must be made to the British Standard Specification.[2]

In the United States the *Library of Congress System*[3] is often used, although its notation is more complex than that of the Dewey Classification to permit very small sub-divisions of a subject. This system uses a combination of letters and figures, the first letter indicating the general class, the second the divisions of a class, and numbers the sub-divisions. The general classes of interest to the R & D worker, for each of which a separate index is published, are:

G   Geography, anthropology
H   Social sciences
Q   Science
R   Medicine
S   Agriculture
T   Technology
U   Military science
V   Naval science
Z   Bibliography, Library science

Another American system is *Bliss's Bibliographic Classification*;[4] this is not used widely, however, owing principally to its comparatively late introduction in 1933.

Classification systems, except perhaps the U.D.C. have in general one inherent fault—they were designed for the general user, and not specifically for the R & D worker who needs to retrieve relevant information from the mass of published material, much of which is in non-book form. In consequence, a method now favoured by many organisations is that of *concept co-ordinate indexing* and in particular the system known commercially by the name *Uniterm*.[5] This method of indexing is based on a vocabulary of *keywords* each of which defines a specific subject; a number of keywords can describe the concepts appearing in a document. In practice, there is a *keycard* for each keyword, on which is entered the serial number (or location code) of each paper in which the keyword appears—information is then retrieved by listing the keywords of the desired subject and determining those papers common to all the keycards. Various commercial systems for recording and extracting the information are available, ranging from simple punched card systems to computer programmes, but it is beyond the scope of this book to describe them. The Uniterm vocabulary, however, appears to be the most favoured, possibly because it is backed by indices that are available commercially.* A similar computer based system, using words in the title, is that known as *KWIC* (Keyword in Context) Indexing.

*Further information is available from Information for Industry Inc., 1000 Connecticut Avenue, Washington 6, D.C. Boston Technical Publishers Inc., Boston, Mass.

Table 11.1. ABSTRACTS BY SUBJECTS

Subject	U.D.C. No.	Abstracts
Science and Technology	5/6	ASLIB Booklist List of Accessions—Science Museum Library Science Progress—Edward Arnold Publishers Ltd
Documentation	5/6:025. 3/4	Journal of Documentation—ASLIB Library Science Abstracts—The Library Association
Translations	5/6:8.03	Index Translationum—UNESCO
Dissertations	5/6(043)	Index to Theses accepted for Higher Degross in the Universities of Gt. Britain and Ireland—ASLIB
Mathematics and Natural Science	5	Current Contents of Space, Electronic and Physical Sciences—Inst. for Scientific Information, Philadelphia, USA
Mathematics	51	Mathematic Gazette—Mathematical Association
Statistics	519	International Journal of Abstracts: Statistical Theory and Method—Oliver & Boyd Ltd
Physics and Mechanics	53	Physics Abstracts (Science Abstracts Section A)—IEE
Mechanics and Rheology	531	Rheology Abstracts—Pergamon Press
Acoustics	534	Journal of the Acoustical Society of America
Optics. Light. Spectra	535	
Heat. Thermodynamics	536	Retrieval Guide to Thermophysical Properties Research Literature, McGraw-Hill
Electricity. Magnetism. Electromagnetism. Solid State Physics	537/538	Electrical Engineering Abstracts (Science Abstracts, Section B)—IEE Semiconductor Abstracts—John Wiley
Nuclear, Atomic and Molecular Physics	539.1	UKAEA List of Publications available to the Public
Chemistry	54	Current Chemical Papers—Chemical Society
Applied Sciences, Technology, Medicine	6	As for 5/6
Patents	608.3	Official Journal (Patents)—Patent Office British Patents Abstracts—Derwent Information Service
Medical Electronics	615.849	Bibliography on Medical Electronics IEEEE
Engineering and Technology	62	British Technology Index—Library Association Engineers' Digest
Materials, Testing, Properties, Corrosion	620.1	ASM Review of Metal Literature—American Society for Metals Bibliographic Surveys of Corrosion—Nat. Assoc. of Corrosion Engineers, Texas, USA
Mechanical and Electrical Eng.	621	As for 537/538 Bibliography and Abstracts on Electrical Contacts—American Society for Testing and Materials
Automatic Control, Automation	621–52	Control Abstracts—IEE

(continued overleaf)

163

Table 11.1. *(continued)*

Subject	U.D.C. No.	Abstracts
Power. Energy	621–8	Direct Energy Conversion Literature Abstracts —US Naval Res. Labs.
Nuclear Technology. Nucleonics	621.039	Nuclear Engineering Abstracts—Silver End Documentary Publications
Electrical Engineering	621.3	ERA Weekly Abstracts—British Electrical and Allied Industries Research Association
Electronics Telecommunications. Radio.	621.38	IEEE Proceedings
Television	621.39	
Vacuum Technology	621.5	Vacuum—Pergamon Press
Mining	622	Abstracts of Current Publications—Safety in Mines. Res. Estb.
Military and Naval Engineering	623	
Civil Engineering	624	
Railways, Roads	625	Monthly Review of Technical Literature— British Railways
Hydraulics	626	Road Abstracts—DSIR
Transport	629	Urban Transportation Research and Planning —US Dept. of Commerce
Automobile	629.113	Monthly Summary of Automobile Engineering Literature—Motor Industry Res. Ass.
Ships	629.12	Journal of the British Shipbuilding Research Association
		Transactions of the Institute of Marine Engineers
Aeronautical	629.13	Index Aeronautics
Management	65	Management Abstracts—BIM
Production Control, Operations Research	658.5	Operational Research Quarterly—Pergamon Press
Chemical Technology	66	Journal of Applied Chemistry—Soc. of Chem. Industry
Glass and Ceramics	666	Glass Technology
		Physics and Chemistry of Glasses
		Transactions of the British Ceramic Society
Metallurgy	669	As for 620.1
		Journal of the Institute of Metals
Ferrous Metals	669.1	Journal of the Iron and Steel Institute
Non-Ferrous Metals	669.2/8	Bulletin of the British Non-Ferrous Metals Research Association
		Nickel Bulletin
		Titanium Abstract Bulletin—ICI
		Platinum Metals Review—Johnson Mattley
Rubber. Plastics	678	Plastic Abstracts
		Plastics
Precision Mechanisms. Instrumentation	681	Instrument Abstracts—BSIRA
		Journal of Scientific Instruments
Computers	681.3	Computer Abstracts—Tech. Inf. Co. Ltd.
		IEEE Transactions of Electronic Computers
Photography	77	Photographic Abstracts—RPS

164

REFERENCE SOURCES

Knowing the classification, it will be possible to ascertain from the card index or catalogue of a library whether there is any relevant material. A more general search may, however, be necessary to cover some or all of the possible sources, which are:

(a) Books
   1. General reference
   2. Subject
   3. Treatise
(b) Periodicals
   1. General, including newspapers
   2. Special
(c) Journals of learned societies
(d) Government publications, including UNO
   1. Published
   2. Restricted because of security
(e) Reports of research organisations and associations
   1. Annual
   2. Special
(f) Manufacturer's literature and pamphlets
(g) Patent publications
(h) Conference proceedings
(i) University theses
(j) Unpublished work

If the information required is already established, specialised reference works such as the following can be of assistance:

(a) *Van Nostrand's Scientific Encyclopedia*
(b) *Handbook of Chemistry and Physics*
(c) *Dictionary of Applied Chemistry*
(d) *Dictionary of Applied Physics*
(e) *Kempe's Engineers Handbook*
(f) *Instruments Manual*
(g) *SIMA Handbook*.

If the information is more than four years old, it may be given in a book, and this can be determined from:

(a) *Cumulative Book Index*, H. W. Wilson Co., USA, (main entry under author; cross entries under subject, alphabetical, and title)
(b) *British National Bibliography*, (cumulative, entries arranged by Dewey Decimal Classification, with author and subject indices)
(c) *A Select List of Standard British Scientific and Technical Books* ASLIB

A *bibliography* will give more complete coverage, and the following can be checked to see if a suitable one has been compiled:

(a) *A World Bibliography of Bibliographies* (1955–6), (this indexes bibliographies under subjects arranged alphabetically)

(b) *Index Bibliographicus,* UNESCO, (periodical abstracts and bibliographies classified by subject and country of origin)

(c) *Bibliographic Index,* (cumulative bibliographies, including articles appearing in books and journals)

(d) Bibliographies on specific subjects are also published by the Science Library and in the USA by the Library of Congress National Bureau of Standards & Armed Services Technical Information Agency, whose lists should be consulted.

For more recent information the lists of *theses* published by universities may be found from:

(a) *Dissertation Abstracts, USA*

(b) *Index to theses, accepted for higher degrees, Universities of Great Britain and Ireland,* ASLIB.

The indices of publications and journals will also have to be scanned, and although the R & D worker should be aware of the more important journals in his field, a check can be made from:

(a) *Willings Press Guide*

(b) *Ulrich's Periodical Directory, USA*

(c) *World List of Scientific Periodicals 1900–1960,* eds. Brown, P., Stratton, G. B., 3 volumes, 4th edition, Butterworth, London (1965).

Searching through periodicals and journals, even if they are readily available, can be very time consuming. The preferred alternative is to scan *abstracts,* the most readily available of which are listed in Table 11.1. There must, however, be a time lag in the process of abstracting, and more up to date information may be obtained from journals such as:

(a) *Current Contents to Space, Electronics and Physical Sciences,* Institute for Scientific Information, Philadelphia. (This gives the contents pages of approximately six hundred research periodicals)

(b) *Current Papers in Physics,* Institute of Electrical Engineers, London

(c) *Current Papers for the Professional Electrical and Electronics Engineer,* Institution of Electrical Engineers, London.

Reports in *Nature* and *Electronic Letters* may also yield recent knowledge.

In making a search, the names of *authors* are most important aids in finding relevant information, and although there is no direct way in which they can be determined, the organisations to which they and other workers belong may possibly be found in:

(a) BALL, I. D. H., *Industrial Research in Britain,* Harrap Research Publications, 5th edit., (1964). (Lists nature of research in Government departments, universities, technical colleges, industrial firms, sponsored organisations; also British periodicals,

English translations of Soviet journals, periodical abstract journals and libraries)

(b) *Scientific Research in British Universities and Colleges,* Ministry of Technology, Annual

(c) BUCKMAN, W. W., *Industrial Research Laboratories of the United States*, Bowker Associates, 12th edit., Washington DC (1965)

(d) *Encyclopedia of Associations*, Gale Res. Co., 3rd edit., Detroit, Michigan. (Lists and gives scope of national, state, and other organisations in USA and Canada)

(e) *Yearbook of International Organisations*, 1964–65, Union of International Associations, 10th edit., Brussels

(f) *Who's Who in International Organisations*, (an index to personnel in the previous publication), International Scientific Organisations, Library of Congress

(g) *Directory of R & D Information Systems*, (1961), (Headquarters Office of Aerospace Research USAF, available through ASTIA (Armed Services Technical Information Agency). Lists centres, services, sources and systems engaged in collecting, storing and disseminating scientific data and information applicable to aerospace research and technology)

(h) *International Guide to European Sources of Technical Information.* Org. for European Economic Co-operation. Encyclopedia of Associations, Gale Research Company, Detroit, (1964)

(i) *A Directory of Information Resources in the United States; Physical Sciences, Biological Sciences, Engineering,* Superintendent of Documents, Government Printing Office, Washington, DC. This gives information on 1100 organisations and institutions throughout the United States

(j) *Roster of U.S. Government Research and Development Contracts in Aerospace and Defence,* compiled by Frost and Sullivan Inc., Bowker Associates Inc., Washington DC (1965).

(k) *Industrial Research Laboratories of the United States,* compiled by Frost and Sullivan Inc., Bowker Associates Inc., Washington DC (1965).

(l) *U.S. Government Research and Development Reports,* published semi-monthly by the Government printing office, Washington, DC. (Lists project title, performing organisation, principal investigator and terms of contract or grant.)

In addition, the Government publications listed in the catalogues of H.M.S.O. and the United States Government Printing Office, together with the annual reports of associations and companies will often be found to yield vital information.

If it can be discovered where the relevant research has been done or is in progress, direct contact should be made, possibly through the public relations office or library, since even if the current status of work is withheld for security reasons, bibliographies and other information may be supplied. Furthermore, duplication of work is to be deprecated.

167

FUNCTIONS OF THE TECHNICAL LIBRARY

The most obvious function of a technical library is to collect, catalogue, and classify information relevant to the organisation of which it is part, and to supply that information to the staff.

It will have been seen from the foregoing section that in a search, all sources of information must be considered and it is obviously impossible for any library to accumulate more than a small proportion. It must, therefore, be a function of the library staff, when a statement of requirements has been made, to make the literature search, and to determine what agencies can assist. A guide to such agencies is given in:

(a) *ASLIB Directory,* 2nd edition, 1957
(b) *Specialised Science Information Services in the United States; A Directory of Selected Specialised Information Services in the Physical and Biological Sciences.* National Science Foundation.

The determination of the most suitable agency is a matter of experience, but the librarian in the United Kingdom can seek the assistance of ASLIB (The Association of Scientific Libraries and Information Bureaux, London) or, in the United States, the Special Libraries Association, NY, and the American Documentation Institute, Washington DC.

When a reference is known, a copy of the publication, if not available, will have to be obtained. Books are normally borrowed, but it is often better to obtain photocopies of periodical articles. In the United Kingdom such a loan service is organised by the National Lending Library for Science and Technology (Boston Spa, Yorkshire), which co-operates with the libraries of local authorities and technical colleges in the loan of books and periodicals. There are a number of such services in the United States, and these are listed in:

Directory of Library Photoduplication Services in the United States, Canada, and Mexico, University of Chicago Library.

For references in foreign languages, the National Lending Library operates a free translation scheme, with the proviso that the translated article is edited. It also co-operates with the United States National Science Foundation in the translation of Russian periodicals, books and articles.

In addition to supplying the scientist with what he requests, the library should also supply him with continuing information. This dissemination of information can consist of the routing of periodicals, marking articles for the attention of individuals, the preparation and circulation of library bulletins, supplemented perhaps by the services of special agencies[6] which use computer techniques for information processing.*

*In the United Kingdom, the National Electronics Research Council is preparing to investigate a system of selective dissemination of information to workers in the electronics field.

The IBM Corporation have devised a system based on co-ordinate indexing, termed 'Current Information Selection' (CIS).[7] Documents are indexed under keywords as described in the previous section, and in addition a 'personal profile' is made for each scientist, using the keywords which describe his interests. All information is stored on punched cards and magnetic tape, from which the profiles of both documents and persons are compared. When a sufficient degree of correlation is obtained a card is forwarded to the scientist, who feeds back information as to whether he has, or has not seen the publication, and whether it is of use.

Another method of dissemination is based on the *Citation Index*, which is defined as 'a directory of cited references where each reference is accompanied by a list of source documents which cite it'. A *Science Citation Index* is now published quarterly, with annual accumulations, by the Institute for Scientific Information (Philadelphia). Such an index has been shown to be one of the most effective sources for compiling a bibliography, but its main defect is that it cannot be entered by subject. A major advantage of the system exists in the 'Advance Science Citation Alert' (ASCA), whereby a scientist can be notified weekly whenever and where, in the journals covered by the service, any references selected by him are cited.

ORGANISATION OF THE TECHNICAL LIBRARY

The R & D manager must ensure that his staff makes full use of all published information, and that money is not wasted in duplicating work. In practice this can only be achieved by treating the library as one of the research divisions, and giving it the necessary status and funds. In consequence the head of the service should be so qualified that he can rank sufficiently high in the management echelon as to advise on policy.

Throughout this chapter the term library has been used synonomously with an internal information service; in many organisations this is combined with the external information service, and may be called upon to serve other divisions within the organisation, as well as outsiders. Furthermore, the library may provide translation services, edit and publish company reports.

The scope and extent of the service given by the library will determine the number and qualifications of the staff. It would appear that to provide a good service, about one professional member and one clerical assistant is required for every one hundred and twenty R & D workers.[8, 9] These figures have been given by American surveys, and appear to be confirmed by a British survey[10] which gives an average of fifty four persons served by each information/library worker. With regard to professional qualifications and training, there are formal courses for librarians in both the United Kingdom and United States, but it should be appreciated that in a technical library other qualifications may be preferred for positions of information officer, literary searcher, abstractor, translator, editor.

The annual budget for the library will depend on management policy and the funds available. In the United States a number of surveys indicate that expenditure may vary from about $250 for each member of the research staff for a small company, to around $700 per member for a large organisation which will probably have extended services. No comparable figures are available for the United Kingdom, but the survey mentioned above indicates that the average expenditure on library documents is 31% of the wages and salaries of the library unit. The budget should cover all expenditure, including salaries, equipment, books, periodicals, subscriptions to special libraries and services, photostats, microfilm, supplies, etc. Recovery is normally made as an overhead charge.

REFERENCES

1. DEWEY, M., *Decimal Classification*, Forest Press, NY, 16th edit. (1958)
2. *B.S. 1000, Universal Decimal Classification*, British Standards Institution, 2nd edit. revised (1957)
3. *Outline of Library of Congress Classification*, Library of Congress, Washington DC (1942)
4. BLISS, H. E., *A Bibliographic Classification, Extended by Systematic Auxiliary Schedules for Composite Specification and Notation*, Wilson NY, 2nd edit. (1952/3)
5. TAUBE, M., *et al*, *Studies in Co-ordinate Indexing*, Documentation Inc., Bethesda, Md. (1953)
6. EAST, H., MARTIN, J., 'Current developments in the dissemination of information', *Bull. Inst. Phys.*, **16**, p. 272, Nov. (1965)
7. MAGINIO, J. J., 'Current information selection by computer', *Industr. Electron.*, **4**, No. 6, p. 269 (1966)
8. HERNER, S., HEATWOLE, M. K., *The Establishment of Staff Requirements in a Small Research Library*, A.C.R.L. Monograph No. 3, Chicago Association of College and Research Libraries (1952)
9. BEDSOLE, D. T., *Library Systems in Large Industrial Corporations*, Dissertation, University of Michigan (1961)
10. *Survey of Information/Library Units in Industrial and Commercial Organisations*, ASLIB (1960)

BIBLIOGRAPHY

STRAURS, L. J., *et al*, *Scientific and Technical Libraries*, Interscience Publications, John Wiley Inc., NY (1964)
Handbook of Special Librarianship—Information Work, ASLIB, 3rd edit. (1967)

Chapter 12

National and International R & D Organisations

The United Kingdom and the United States Governments spend a very large part of their national incomes on R & D. Such Government sponsored research may be carried out in Governmental laboratories, under contract by commercial organisations, or by making grants to universities and research associations.

In both countries, approximately 65% of all R & D is Government financed. It is evident, therefore, that there are few fields in which some Government agency or establishment has not an interest; if not a potential customer, it may at least be a source of information as to the latest practice, although in defence, naturally, the dissemination of information may be subject to security restrictions.

Both Governments may also perform a third role, that of co-ordinating and sponsoring industrial research in specific industries.

In certain areas of research, *international organisations* have been formed. These organisations may be financed either through UNO or by direct Government grants.

This chapter delineates the organisational structures, to acquaint the R & D manager with those agencies relevant to his sphere of work, so that he can take action to make the necessary contacts.

UNITED KINGDOM ORGANISATIONS

DEFENCE R & D

The Defence Council of the *Ministry of Defence* formulates the broad policy for R & D. This policy is founded upon the advice of the Chief Scientific Adviser to the Ministry and the operational requirements of the Service Departments, the ministers of which are individually responsible for various fields.

Within the Service Departments, the responsibility is shared between the executive and research establishments. The executive is responsible for formulating operational requirements and for approving the programme of work proposed by the research establishment. The executive may be comprised of service personnel and/or civilians. It will also work in close liaison with the production branch, since the aim is always to develop equipment suitable for use by the armed forces.

The Admiralty Board of the Defence Council is advised on scientific matters primarily by the Chief Scientist (Royal Navy) and the Controller of the Navy. Responsible to the Chief Scientist is the Chief of the Royal Naval Scientific Service, who administers all scientific personnel and those research establishments which are not concerned directly with weapons. The Director Generals for Weapons (naval), Ships, and Aircraft (naval) report directly to the Controller, the research departments under the first two being controlled jointly by the relevant department, in this case the executive, and the R.N.S.S. This ensures liaison between the potential user and designer. In areas of research carried out by other service departments, only the executive may have a direct interest as, for example, naval aircraft and equipment. Within the Navy Department, the Director of Physical Research is responsible for co-ordinating R & D on electronic valves and semiconductor devices to meet the requirements of all Government departments and also of the Post Office; the latter, however, due to its special requirements, may initiate work separately and issue its own specifications.

The Army Department is organised in a similar manner, the two senior officers mainly responsible for scientific research being the Chief Scientist (Army), and the Master General of the Ordnance. Research establishments under the Army Department are engaged primarily on munitions, clothing, vehicles, chemical warfare and operational research to meet the requirements for all three service departments.

The Air Force Department is responsible for R & D only in meteorology and aviation medicine. There is, however, a Chief Scientist (Royal Air Force) whose staff advises on research policy.

The procurement of aircraft, guided missiles, atomic weapons, and electronic equipment is the function of the Ministry of Technology which co-ordinates the requirements of the three service departments within the Ministry of Defence.

Table 12.1 lists the research establishments which may or may not be administered by the parallel executive or policy department; in either event there will be close liaison with the executive department, and either through it or directly, with other departments and establishments having similar interests.

The above describes briefly the vertical organisation of the defence ministries, but equally important is the horizontal organisation, both within a particular ministry and between the ministries.

For certain projects, permanent inter-service committees are in existence, an example in the electronic field being CVD (Co-ordination of Valve Development), which is administered by the Navy Department, and RCRDC (Radio Components Research and Development Committee), the secretariat of which is provided by the Ministry of Technology, Electronic Research and Development Division. After the design approval stage, co-ordination is continued by TVC (Technical Valve Committee), and RCSC (Radio Component Specification Committee).

MINISTRY OF TECHNOLOGY

The Ministry of Technology is responsible for the major part of the United Kingdom Government expenditure on R & D in both the industrial and defence fields, where it has the object of increasing the value of this research to industry. It is organised into three groups, as follows:

(a) *Engineering*, which contains the following five divisions:
1. Electronics and instruments
2. Computers
3. Machine tools, manufacturing machinery and automation
4. Vehicles and mechanical engineering products
5. Electrical, chemical and shipbuilding industries

    For a particular industry, these divisions are the main point of contact with the Government, and their functions involve examination of problems and identifying measures which can help solve them. At the same time, these divisions are concerned with the technological progress of the industry.
(b) *Research*, the head of which, as the Chief Scientist, is the professional head of the scientific staff in the department, and responsible for the strategy and co-ordination of the research programmes of all the R & D establishments and research stations.
(c) *Aviation*. This group is responsible for the procurement of aircraft, guided weapons, electronic and other equipment, both military and civil, including exports.

    It has responsibility for the sponsorship of the aerospace industry and its re-organisation. It also has certain executive responsibilities for the work done in the defence research establishments under the control of the Research Group, the divisions concerned being:
1. Scientific Research (Air) and Future Aircraft
2. Civil Aircraft and General Services R & D
3. Engine R & D
4. R.N. Aircraft and Helicopter Development
5. Flying R & D
6. Atomic Weapons Development
7. Aircraft Equipment R & D
8. Guided Weapons R & D
9. Space R & D
10. Electronics R & D

173

Table 12.1. U.K. DEFENCE R & D EXECUTIVE DEPARTMENTS AND ESTABLISHMENTS

Executive	Research Establishment	General fields of interest, if not obvious in title
Ministry of Defence, Navy Department		
(a) Chief of the Royal Naval Scientific Service		
1. Director Physical Research (Navy)	Admiralty Res. Lab., Teddington (ARL)	Objective basic research, e.g. nucleonics, acoustics
	Services Electronic Res. Lab. (SERL)	Objective basic and applied research in electronic techniques and semi-conductors
	Services Valve Test Lab., Haslemere, Surrey (SVTL)	
	Royal Naval Physiological Lab., Alverstoke, Hants	
2. Director of Material Research (DMR)	Admiralty Material Lab., Holton Heath, Dorset (AML)	Metallurgy, ceramics, plastics
3. Director of R & D Services		
(b) Director General Weapons (Naval)		
1. Director of Weapons, Surface	Admiralty Surface Weapons Establishment, Portsmouth (ASWE)	Admiralty design authorities for electronic components, including valves and techniques.
2. Director of Weapons, Radio		Communication systems, radar, navigational aids. Gunnery and guided weapon systems
3. Director of Weapons, Underwater	Admiralty Underwater Weapons Establishment, Portland (AUWE)	Sonar, mine design
4. Director of Weapons, Compass	Admiralty Compass Observatory, Slough Bucks (ACO)	Compasses, chronometers, inertial navigational equipment
5. Director of Weapons, Naval Ordnance, Inspection	Depots at various places	Inspection of naval equipment
(c) Director General of Ships		
1. Director of Naval Construction		
2. Director of Marine Engineering		
3. Director of Naval Electrical E…		

1. Director of Air Equipment and Photography	
2. Director of Aircraft Electrics and Armaments	
Army Department	
(a) Chief Scientist (Army)	
1. Electronics Adviser to Chief Scientist (Army)	
2. Deputy Chief Scientist (Army)	
3. Director of Army Operational Research	Defence Operational Research Analysis Establishment, West Byfleet, Surrey
(b) Master-General of the Ordnance	
1. Director General of Artillery	Royal Armament R & D Establishment, Sevenoaks, Kent (RARDE)
2. Director General of Armaments	
3. Director of Biological and Chemical Defence	Chemical Defence Research Establishment Microbiological Research Establishment, Porton, Nr. Salisbury, Wilts
4. Director General of Fighting Vehicles	Fighting Vehicles Research Establishment, Chertsey, Surrey (FVRDE)
5. Director of Royal Engineer Equipment	Military Engineering Experimental Establishment, Christchurch, Hants (See Min. Tech.—SRDE)
6. Director of Army Communication and Electronic Equipment	Clothing and Stores Experimental Establishment, Farnborough, Hants
Air Force Department in conjunction with the Navy Department	
(a) Director General of Meteorological Office	Met. Office, London, and Bracknell, Berks In association with NERC
(b) Director General of RAF Medical Services	Inst. of Aviation Medicine, Farnborough, Hants

Table 12.2. MINISTRY OF TECHNOLOGY R & D ESTABLISHMENTS

Research Establishments	*Address*	*General fields of interest*
Royal Aircraft Establishment (RAE)	Farnborough, Hants	Aerodynamics, research on metals and structures, aircraft traffic controls and navigation systems including inertial navigation, optics, automatic control systems for aircraft and engineering processes, electronic computing and data processing, plasma and solid-state physics, radio, and research
Royal Radar Establishment (RRE)	Malvern, Worcs	Radar and microwave techniques, navigation radar, automatic guidance and control, electronic physics, computer research and data handling, electronic component research, solid-state and microelectronics, GW and space research
Signals Research and Development Establishment (SRDE)	Christchurch, Hants	Communication links, speech analysis and synthesis, electronic nuclear physics. Batteries and power supplies
National Gas Turbine Establishment (NGTE)	Pyestock, Hants	Aerodynamics, noise generation and propagation, heat transfer, combustion processes, properties of materials at high temperatures, instrumentation, data handling
Explosives Research and Development Establishment (ERDE)	Waltham Abbey, Essex	Chemical engineering, physics of solids, molecular structure, infra-red spectroscopy, rocket propellants
Aeroplane and Armament Experimental Establishment (AAEE)	Boscombe Down, Wilts	Flight testing and assessment of aircraft, navigational aids, weapons
Rocket Propulsion Establishment (RPE)	Westcott, Bucks	Properties of hot gases and plasmas, hydrodynamics, heat transfer, control systems
Research Stations		
H.Q.	Millbank Tower, S.W.1	Administers British Calibration Service. Collaborates with British Standards Institution
		Administers Production Engineering Advisory Service in collaboration with PERA
Building Research Station	Garston, Herts	Building science, heating and ventilation
Fire Research Station (FRS)	Borehamwood, Herts	Initiation, growth and suppression of fire, materials fire-fighting equipment
Forest Products Res. Lab. (FPRL)	Princes Risborough, Bucks	Properties, preservation and uses of timber, including pulp
Government Chemist	Waterloo, S.W.1	Advises on chemical matters to various departments of state in particular the

viaducts)

National Engineering Laboratory	East Kilbride, Glasgow	Materials, mechanics of solids and fluids, lubrication, mechanism, metrology noise, heat transfer, forming and shaping materials, thermodynamics
National Physical Laboratory (now includes the National Chemical Lab.)	Teddington Middx	Aerodynamics, applied physics, autonomics, basic physics, light, mathematics, ships, standards
Torry Research Station	Aberdeen	Transport and storage of fish
Warren Spring Laboratory	Stevenage, Herts	Mineral processing, chemical engineering, atmospheric pollution, human sciences
Water Pollution Research Laboratory	Stevenage, Herts	Pollution of water supplies, sewage, industrial effluents

Atomic Energy

H.Q.	London, S.W.1	
Atomic Weapons Research Establishment, (AWRE)	Aldermaston, Berks	Refer Defence R & D. Development of nuclear warheads and supporting research. Nuclear research and certain work in civil nuclear programme
Radio Chemical Centre	Amersham, Bucks	Production and marketing of radioisotopes
Capenhurst Works	Capenhurst, Chester	Development of uranium enrichment processes and operation of gaseous diffusion plant
Chapelcross Works	Annan, Dumfriesshire	Experimental fuel irradiation and radiological research Training service for reactor operators
Culham Laboratory	Abingdon, Berks	Research into plasma physics and controlled thermo-nuclear fusion
Atomic Energy Research Establishment (AERE)	Harwell, Berks	Long term research into non-military aspects of atomic energy. Basic research in materials, physics, chemistry, metallurgy, electronics, health physics and chemical engineering
Risley	Warrington, Lancs	H.Q. of Engineering, Production and Reactor Group technical and economic studies
Dounreay, Experimental Reactor Group	Thurso, Caithness	Development of fast reactors, including fabrication and reprocessing of fuel
Springfield Works and Laboratory	Preston, Lancs	Development of fuels and fuel elements
Wantage Research Laboratory	Wantage, Berks	Isotope Research
Windscale and Calder Works	Seascale, Cumberland	Operation of production reactors and chemical separation of fuel
Winfrith Atomic Energy Establishment	Winfrith, Dorchester	Theoretical and experimental aspects of reactor physics, and kinetics

Table 12.2 lists the establishments and stations for which the Ministry is responsible. The *establishments* are concerned primarily with defence, whilst the broad policy for the *stations* is to undertake research, to help central and local Government authorities to provide necessary services for the nation, to supply basic data for industry and improve techniques available to industry as a whole. Work on a repayment basis may be undertaken to solve specific industrial problems.

The Ministry is responsible for the *United Kingdom Atomic Energy Authority*, which in 1965 had its charter extended to permit it to undertake work outside the atomic field, an example being the development of water desalination processes. It is also responsible for the *National Research Development Corporation*, which was established to promote and finance in the public interest the development of inventions, particularly those resulting from research carried out by Government departments, or paid for by public money, although in certain circumstances it may also assist private inventors.

The Ministry aids, by means of grants, forty eight *industrial research associations* which are listed in Table 12.3. These associations are autonomous bodies, governed by a council elected by the members, with the exception of two nominated by the Ministry; all members of the council are closely associated with the particular industry concerned. The research associations are usually concerned with co-operative research, the competitive research being undertaken by the individual companies. This means that the associations are normally concerned more with objective basic research and applied research, both project and operational, rather than development. An association may, however, carry out specific research on behalf of a member on a fee paying basis.

The Ministry of Technology has a number of regional offices which are responsible for encouraging technical development in the industries in their areas, and for promoting effective co-operation between industry and Government, academic and independent establishments concerned with R & D and assisting industry to make greater use of existing scientific and technical knowledge. In pursuance of this policy these offices co-ordinate the *Industrial Liaison Centres*, which are normally based on Colleges of Advanced Technology, and regional and area technical colleges. A nationwide *British Calibration Service* has been established, and at the same time standards are being aligned in collaboration with the *British Standards Institution*. The *Production Engineering Advisory Service,* operated on behalf of the Ministry by the *Production Engineering Research Association,* has also been formed.

NON-INDUSTRIAL R & D

The *Council for Scientific Policy* advises the Secretary of State for Education and Science with reference to his responsibility for the formulation and execution of Government scientific policy; this includes the balance of scientific effort in the various non-industrial fields for which he is responsible. The execution of policy is carried out through the research councils listed below, who collaborate with the other Ministries concerned, for example, Ministry of Health, Ministry of Agriculture, Fisheries and Food:

(a) Science Research Council (SRC)
(b) Medical Research Council (MRC)
(c) Agricultural Research Council (ARC)
(d) Natural Environment Research Council (NERC)

Each council is advised by a number of technical committees, through which they control the various research institutes, establishments, and units shown in Table 12.4. In addition, the Science Research Council administers research grants and postgraduate training awards at universities. It is responsible for the scientific space research programme, and advises on relations with the *European Space Research Organisation* (ESRO)*, and also the *European Centre for Nuclear Research* (CERN).

Certain other Ministries, as shown in Table 12.4, have their own research establishments, but even if there are none there is usually a scientific adviser's office, the function of which is to advise on scientific aspects of departmental policy and to define problems calling for research.

In addition to the above research establishments, there are a number operated by the nationalised industries and public corporations and these are listed in Table 12.5.

UNITED STATES FEDERAL ORGANISATION FOR SCIENTIFIC ACTIVITIES

The *Federal Organisation for Science* consists of components of both the Executive and Legislative Branches of the Federal Government. In the Executive Branch, ten departments and twenty seven independent agencies contain units which plan, administer, conduct or support scientific activities. Within the Legislative Branch are Congressional Committees, the Library of Congress, the Botanic Garden and the Government Printing Office, all engaged in scientific activities. These agencies range widely in size, functions, fields of science, types of scientific and technological activities supported, contact with non-Government institutions, and types of facilities.

A number of agencies were established primarily to promote some aspect of science and technology, for example, the National Aeronautics and Space Administration and the Atomic Energy Commission which emphasise engineering development. Appropriate scientific activities in other departments and agencies are performed at the bureau level on a large scale. Under the Department of Commerce, for example, are

*The Ministry of Technology is responsible for certain aspects of space research and for co-ordination with the *European Launcher Development Organisation* (E.L.D.O.).

Table 12.3. UNITED KINGDOM RESEARCH ASSOCIATIONS

Research Association	Address	General fields of interest
British Baking Assoc.	Chorleywood, Herts	All aspects of bread, biscuits and flour confectionary flour including botany and biochemistry of cereals
Shoe and Allied Trades Research Association	Kettering, Northants	Materials, manufacture, design
British Brush Manufacturers Association	The University, Leeds	Design of bristle brushes
British Cast Iron Research Association	Alvechurch, Birmingham	All aspects of ironfounding
British Ceramic Research Association	Stoke-on-Trent	Pottery, refractories, ceramics, in particular high temperature
Civil Engineering Research Association	London, S.W.1	Initiates and supports research in all fields
Welwyn Hall Research Association	Welwyn, Herts	Calcareous products, industrial powders
British Coal Utilisation Research Association	Leatherhead, Surrey	Combustion and non-fuel uses
British Coke Research Association	Chesterfield, Derbyshire	Fundamental investigation into formation and properties and structure
Cotton, Silk and Man-made Fibres Research Association	Didsbury, Manchester	Structure, properties and utilisation of fibres including spinning, dyeing, weaving etc.
Cutlery and Allied Trades Research Association	Sheffield	Production of cutlery and small tools with cutting edges
Drop Forging Research Association	Sheffield 3	All aspects, including economics
Electrical Research Association	Leatherhead, Surrey	Generation, transmission, switchgear, transformers, insulation, dielectrics, utilisation
File Research Council	Sheffield 3	Metallurgy, physical characteristics, manufacture
British Food Manufacturing Industries Research Association	Leatherhead, Surrey	All aspects of processed foods, emphasis on new materials, control of processes and products

180

Association	Location	Research
Fruit and Vegetable Preservation Research Association	Chipping Campden, Gloucester	Canning, deep freezing, dehydration—biochemical and microbiological studies
Furniture Industry Research Association	Stevenage, Herts	Production, finishing
Gelatine and Glue Research Association	Birmingham, 12	Chemistry and physics, new derivatives
British Glass Industry Research Association	Sheffield, 10	Materials, processes, products
Heating and Ventilating Research Association	Bracknell, Berks	Design and performance of heating, ventilating and air conditioning systems
Hosiery and Allied Trades Research Association	Nottingham	Materials, processes and techniques of knitting
British Hydromechanics Research Association	Cranfield, Bedfordshire	Fluid mechanics, fluid machines, valves, seals, glands, metering, transport of solids in fluids. Fluid power and oil hydraulics
British Industrial Biological Research Association	Carshalton, Surrey	Toxicological testing of food additives, effects of insecticides, etc. Also cosmetics, job evaluation, ergometrics, personnel selection
British Iron and Steel Research Association Laboratories	H.Q. London, S.W.1	All aspects of iron and steel making
British Jute Trade Research Association	Dundee, Scotland	All operations from new jute and alternatives to finished cloth
Lace Research Association	Bilborough, Notts	Manufacture, new fibres, products
British Launderers' Research Association	Hendon, London, N.W.4	All aspects of cleaning including bacteriology
British Leather Manufacturers' Research Association	Egham, Surrey	Preservation, preparation, performance in manufacture and use
Linen Industry Research Association	Co. Antrim, N. Ireland	All aspects from flax production to finished linen
Machine Tool Industry Research Association	Macclesfield, Cheshire	Performance, design
Motor Industry Research Association	Nuneaton, Warwick	All aspects of cars and commercial vehicles
Commonwealth Mycological Institute	Kew, Surrey	Industrial fungi and their use. Control of moulds

(continued overleaf)

181

Table 12.3. *(continued)*

Research Association	Address	General fields of interest
British Non-Ferrous Metals Research Association	London, N.W.1	Extraction, properties, fabrication, surface finishing of non-ferrous metals
Research Association of British Paint, Colour and Varnish Manufacturers	Teddington,	Chemistry and Manufacture
Paper and Board, Printing and Packaging Industry	Kenley, Surrey	All aspects
Printing, Packaging and Allied Trades Research Association	Leatherhead, Surrey	Printing, Book-binding, paper, ink, adhesives, packaging etc
Production Engineering Research Association of G.B.	Melton Mowbray, Leicester	R & D on all aspects of manufacture. Operates on Production Engineering Advisory Service
Rubber and Plastics Research Association of G.B.	Shrewsbury,	Properties, processes, uses
British Scientific Instrument Research Association	Chislehurst, Kent	Measurement and control techniques. Instrumentation mechanics
British Ship Research Association	London, S.E.1	Ship structure and design, propulsion
Spring Manufacturers Research Association	Sheffield 3	Design, manufacture, testing
British Steel Casting	Sheffield 2	Steelmaking, foundry processes, moulding materials
Coal Tar Research Association	Gomersal, Leeds	Refining, provision of new outlets and new materials
Timber Research and Development Association	High Wycombe, Bucks	Applications, design of structures, plywood etc.
Water Research Association	Marlow, Bucks	All aspects of water supply
British Welding Research Association	Abington, Cambridge	Development, application, control, processes and techniques
Wool Industries Research Association	Headingley, Leeds 6	Wool utilisation

the Patent Office, the National Bureau of Standards, the Coast and Geodetic Survey, the Weather Bureau, the Office of Business Economics and the Bureau of the Census. Many of these organisations in turn contain subordinate divisions which make contributions in their fields to science. These subordinate divisions may be *installations, field stations*, and *research centres*. An installation is equivalent to the British 'establishment', being defined as a substantially self-contained organisation, usually separated geographically from the agency or unit to which it reports, and employing more than a hundred persons who are engaged in scientific activities. A field station, in contrast, is a relatively small organisational unit. Federal Contract Research Centres are R & D undertakings, financed exclusively or substantially by the Government, which in most instances were established initially to meet an R & D need of the Federal Government. They are administered by a private organisation through a contractual arrangement; the administration may be by a profit organisation, an educational institution, or by some other group or private organisation. As the total of installations, field stations, and research centres run into many hundreds it is not practical to list them, and the reader is referred to:

(a) *Federal Organisation for Scientific Activities,* National Science Foundation
(b) *Aerospace and Defense Research Contracts Roster,* 1965. Frost & Sullivan Inc., Bowker Associates Inc. (1966)

From these can be determined the agencies, bureaux, and locations carrying out scientific activities within a particular field of interest.

The review and supervision of Federal scientific programmes at the Presidential level is carried out through the *Office of Science and Technology,* which may assist in the formulation of policies in science and technology. In addition, the Special Assistant to the President for Science and Technology is responsible for keeping the President informed of the progress of scientific and technical efforts in Federal agencies and for presenting the findings, evaluations, and recommendations. The President's *Science Advisory Committee* is responsible for providing answers to questions raised by the President, and for recommending ways in which United States science and technology can be advanced. The *Federal Council of Science and Technology* considers Federal scientific and technological problems and developments affecting more than one Federal agency.

Within most of the agencies at Secretary level there is an engineer or scientist to direct and co-ordinate scientific activities. This means that there is a staff science administrator at a level above that of bureaux or major sub-divisions, which have operating responsibilities in R & D. Such an administrator has authority and supervision over subordinate units, as well as the responsibility for co-ordinating their scientific programmes. Generally, these science administrators have authority to examine scientific requirements and 'review' agency-wide policy; they

Table 12.4. NON-INDUSTRIAL SCIENTIFIC R & D EXECUTIVE DEPARTMENTS AND ESTABLISHMENTS

Executive	Establishment	Address	General fields of interest if not obvious in title
Department of Education and Science	National Lending Library	Whitehall	Control of scientific attachés
		Boston Spa, Yorkshire	
Agricultural Research Council	Animal Physiology Inst.	Regent Street, W.1	
	Animal Breeding Res.	Babraham, Cambs	
	Ditton Lab.	Edinburgh 9	
	Institute for Research on Animal Diseases	Maidstone, Kent	Fruits
	Pest Infestation Lab.	Compton, Berks	
	Poultry Res. Centre	Slough, Bucks	
	Radiological Lab.	Edinburgh 9	
	Weed Res. Lab.	Wantage, Berks	
	Food Research Institute	Kidlington, Oxford	
	Meat Research Institute	Norwich	
	also: 22 Res. Units	Cambridge	
Medical Research Council	National Institute for Medical Research	Westminster, S.W.1	Responsible to Ministry of Health for standards and control of therapeutic substances
		Mill Hill, N.W.7	Physiology, pharmacology, chemo-therapy, virology, biochemistry
	also: 43 Res. Units 22 Res. Groups	Chichester, Sussex	Medical electronics, biomechanics

184

Organisation	Establishment	Address	Functions
Science Research Council	Atlas Computer Laboratory Rutherford High Energy Lab. Daresbury Nuclear Physics Lab. Radio and Space Res. Station	State House, High Holborn, W.C.1 Didcot, Berks Harwell Warrington, Lancs Slough, Bucks	Administers University grants, collaborates with E.S.R.O. and C.E.R.N.
	Royal Greenwich Observatory Also: Astronomical Observatories	Herstmonceux, Sussex	Tracking and telemetry as an N.A.S.A. station
National Environment Research Council	Nature Conservancy, Research Branch National Inst. of Oceanography Institute of Geological Sciences Hydrological Research Unit	State House, High Holborn W.C.1 Belgrave Square, S.W.1 Hope Terrace, Edinburgh Witley, Surrey South Kensington, S.W.7 Wallingford, Berks	Geophysics survey methods Basic research on action of rivers, tides and waves; civil engineering (harbours, viaducts)
Ministry of Power Chief Scientist Div.	Safety in Mines Research Establishment: Central Lab. Field Lab.	Millbank, S.W.1 Sheffield Buxton	

(continued overleaf)

Table 12.4 continued

Executive	Establishment	Address	General fields of interest if not obvious in title
Ministry of Transport	Road Res. Lab. Road Res. Lab.	West Drayton, Middlesex Langley, Bucks	ASWE extension, Eastney, advises on merchant marine radar and navigational aids Materials and construction Traffic and safety division
Board of Trade	Telecommunications Engineering Estb. (TEE)	Victoria Street, S.W.1 Gatwick, Surrey	Assessment and testing of telecommunications. Navigational aids and radar used by civil aircraft
Corporation of Trinity House	Dept. of the Engineer in Chief Research Station	Tower Hill, E.C.3 Dungeness	Shipping aids e.g. lights, foghorns, radar beacons
Ministry of Agriculture Fisheries and Food Fishery Research Directorate	Information Division Plant Pathology Laboratory Veterinary Laboratories Infestation Control Laboratory Fisheries Laboratories Shellfish Laboratories Salmon and Freshwater Fisheries Laboratory	Whitehall Place, S.W.1 Whitehall Place, S.W.1 Harpenden, Herts Weybridge, Surrey Surbiton, Surrey Lowestoft, Suffolk Burnham-on-Crouch, Essex Whitehall Place, S.W.1	

Department/Organisation	Establishment	Location	Notes
Department of Agriculture and Fisheries for Scotland		Edinburgh 1	
	Fisheries Research Marine Laboratory	Torry, Aberdeen	
	Freshwater Fisheries Laboratory	Pitlochry, Perthshire	
Forestry Commission	Director of Research Research Station	Saville Row, W.1 Farnham, Surrey	In association with N.E.R.C.
Royal Mint	Assay Office	Tower Hill, E.C.3	New alloys, die steels, new methods of coin production
Ministry of Works Chief Mech. and Elec. Eng. Div.		Lambeth, S.E.1	
Home Office Scientific Adviser's Branch	Central Res. Lab. in Forensic Science Home Office Regional Lab. 7 Regional Laboratories	Whitehall, S.W.1 and various Aldermaston, Bucks Aldermaston, Bucks	Communications, civil defence
Ministry of Overseas Development	Tropical Products Institute	Gt. Smith St., S.W.1 Gray's Inn Road, W.C.1	Geophysics Chemical investigations, pest control, physical and engineering work (e.g. power generation)
Foreign Office	Government Communications Headquarters, (G.C.H.Q.) Government Communications Centre,	Cheltenham, Glos Bedford	

Table 12.5. UNITED KINGDOM NATIONALISED INDUSTRIES AND PUBLIC CORPORATIONS

Authority	Address	Main fields of interest
National Coal Board Research and Development Establishment	Stanhope Bretby, nr. Burton-on-Trent	Mining techniques, mechanical engineering, coal preparation, design, construction, electrical engineering, physics
Central Electricity Generating Board	Waterloo, S.W.1	Chief Research and Development Officer
Research Laboratories	Leatherhead, Surrey	Basic research
Engineering Laboratories	Marchwood, Southampton	Large scale prototype and development
Berkeley Laboratories*	Berkeley, Glos.	Nuclear research and development distribution, application and utilisation
British Transport Commission	Marylebone Road, N.W.1 Derby	Director Chemistry, operational research, engineering, communication and signalling systems, data handling, physics, metallurgy, textiles
British Railways, Research Department	Muswell Hill, N.10	
London Transport Research Laboratory	Chiswick, W.4	
British Broadcasting Corporation Research Laboratories	Kingswood Warren, Evesham, Worcs.	Acoustics, recording, transmitters and aerials, field strength and propagation, receivers and radio frequency. Measurements, microphones and loudspeakers
The Gas Council Basic Research Group	Fulham, London	Chemical engineering, catalysts, control systems
London Research Station	Fulham, London	
Post Office Headquarters Research Laboratories	Gresham St. W.C.1 Dollis Hill, London	All aspects of communication including basic research

*A new laboratory is planned. At present, this work is being carried out partly by C.E.G.B. laboratories and those of Area Boards, and partly by sub-contract to outside laboratories.

Table 12.6. MAJOR INTERNATIONAL SCIENTIFIC ORGANISATIONS

	Organisation	Address	Main fields of interest
UNESCO	United Nations Educational, Scientific and Cultural Organisation	Place de Fontenoy, Paris 7^e	Joint study of problems beyond the means of any one country, e.g. hydrology, oceanography, seismology, scientific maps, geophysics, space science
OECD	Organisation for Economic Co-operation and Development	Château de la Muette, 2, Rue André-Pascal, Paris 16^e	Technological development (production engineering, metallurgy); conservation and exploitation of natural resources; preservation and improvement of materials; safeguarding of public health
NATO	North Atlantic Treaty Organisation	Porte Dauphine, Paris 16^e	Oceanography, operations research, meteorology, human factors, quantum electronics, aeronautical research (AGARD), defence (SHAPE), anti-submarine warfare (La Spezia)
IAEA	International Atomic Energy Agency	11 Kärntnerring, Vienna 1	Nuclear energy studies, health safety and waste disposal
ENEA	European Nuclear Energy Agency	38 Boulevard Suchet, Paris 16^e	Harmonisation of programmes, regulation and control, exchange of information (e.g. neutronic data) analysis of costs etc.
Eurochemic	European Company for the Chemical Processing of Irradiated Fuels	Mol, Belgium	Extraction of the constituents of irradiated fuels, purification of plutonium
Halden	Halden Reactor	Halden, Norway	Technical and industrial possibilities of this type of reactor
Dragon	'Dragon' Reactor	Atomic Energy Establishment Winfrith, U.K.	Development and operation of reactor. Studies arising from high temperature reactors
CERN	European Organisation for Nuclear Research	Meyrin, Geneva	Research on high energy particles, including work on cosmic rays. Research involving a proton synchroton, and a synchro-cyclotron. Theoretical nuclear physics
EURATOM	European Atomic Energy Community	53 Rue Belliard, Brussels	Development of various types of reactors, study of controlled thermonuclear reactions, research on effects of radiation and their application. Four res. estbs. are operated under the Joint Nuclear Research Centre

(continued overleaf)

Table 12.6 *continued*

	Organisation	Address	Main fields of interest
ESRO	European Space Research Organisation	36 Rue La Pérouse, Paris 16ᵉ (provisional HQ)	Launching of sounder rockets, orbital satellites, space probes, and associated research possibilities
ELDO	European Space Vehicle Launcher Development Organisation	36 Rue La Pérouse, Paris 16ᵉ (provisional HQ)	Joint construction of a three stage space vehicle launcher, study of future possibilities
WMO	World Meteorological Organisation	41 Avenue Giuseppa-Motta, Geneva	Promotes research in meteorology, participates in international programmes
IIR	International Institute of Refrigeration	177 Boulevard Malesherbes, Paris 17ᵉ	Scientific problems relating to low temperatures, thermometry, insulating materials, refrigerating machinery, applications
BIPM	International Bureau of Weights and Measures	Pavillon de Breteuil, Sèvres, Seine-et-Oise, France	Standards. Studies for improving high precision instruments and measurements
ICC	International Computation Centre	Palazzo degli Uffici, Villa della Civiltà del Lavoro 23, Rome-EUR	Research projects are mostly confined to computer software
ECSC	European Coal and Steel Community	2 Place de Metz, Luxembourg	Mining technology, applications and utilisation of coal. Applied research on iron ore and steel, including the application of new techniques
OEEPE	European Organisation for Experimental Photogrammetric Research	I.T.C. Kanaalweg, Delft, Netherlands	Precision photogrammetry in civil engineering, development and automation of methods. Cartography
ICSU	International Council of Scientific Unions	2 Via Sebenico, Rome	Co-ordinating and development centre for all branches of the fundamental sciences. Various organisations and committees are attached to the Council for specific areas of work
	Zoological Station of Naples	Villa Comunale, Naples	Marine invertebrate tissue cultures, metallo-protein constitution, physiology, enzyme action etc.
	Jungfraujoch Scientific Station	Bühlplatz 5, Berne (Secretarial)	All branches of science requiring high altitude research

Fig. 12.1. *Methods of action of international scientific organisations. Reproduced from International Scientific Organisations, by courtesy of the Organisation for Economic Co-operation and Development*

ORGANISATIONS	ORGANISATIONS — WITH LABORATORIES — OF THEIR OWN	WITH LABORATORIES — ASSOCIATED or JOINT	WITHOUT LABORATORIES	CO-OPERATIVE RESEARCH PROGRAMMES — UNDER CONTRACT WITH ONE OR MORE NATIONAL TEAMS	CENTRALISED IN ONE OF THE LABORATORIES — WITH GRANTS	CENTRALISED — WITHOUT GRANTS	DECENTRALISED — WITH GRANTS	DECENTRALISED — WITHOUT GRANTS	CO-ORDINATION OF PROGRAMMES	PROMOTION OF RESEARCH — FELLOWSHIPS AND TRAINING COURSES	GENERAL SERVICES (DOCUMENTATION, STATISTICS, MEASUREMENTS, ETC.)	ORGANISATION OF MEETINGS (SEMINARS, SYMPOSIA, CONFERENCES, ETC.)	SCIENTIFIC AID TO LESS-DEVELOPED COUNTRIES
INTER-GOVERNMENTAL													
UNESCO			○		○		○		●	○	○	○	●
OECD			○			○		●	○	○	○	○	○
NATO	○	○		○	●		○			●	○	○	●
IAEA	●	○		○	○	○	○	○	○	○	○	○	
ENEA	●	●								○	○	○	
EUROCHEMIC	●			○							○	○	
HALDEN	●			○							○	○	
DRAGON	●			○							○	○	
CERN	●	○							○	○	○	○	
EURATOM	●			●	○		○		○	○	●	●	
ESRO	●	○		○	○		○		○	○	○	○	
ELDO		○		●	○		○		●	○	○	●	
WMO			○								●	○	
IIR			○									○	○
BIPM	○										●	●	
ICC	●								○		○	○	
ECSC			○				●		●	○	○	○	○
NON-GOVERNMENTAL													
OEEPE			○					●			○	○	
ICSU			○					○			○	●	
ZOOLOGICAL STATION OF NAPLES	●											○	
JUNGFRAUJOCH SCIENTIFIC STATION	●												

● PRINCIPAL METHODS OF ACTION   ○ OTHER METHODS OF ACTION

also make programme decisions, apportioning agency funds and man-power. In addition, they have the necessary status to participate effectively in inter-agency decision making and in Congressional proceedings.

Within the bureaux and major sub-divisions, the responsibility for integration and co-ordination of the administration, planning and conduct of scientific programmes is usually centralised in an 'Office'. Such programmes may then be carried out in installations, field stations, research centres, or under contract by universities or industrial concerns.

Although in the United States there are no equivalents to the United Kingdom Government sponsored industrial research organisations, there are a very large number of non-profit research institutes, centres, foundations, laboratories, bureaux, experimental stations, and other organisations. These are listed, together with their fields of interest, in:

Research Centers Directory, Gale Research Company, Michigan, 2nd. edit. (1965)

INTERNATIONAL R & D ORGANISATIONS

From the birth of modern science in the 18th century there has been international co-operation, but it is only since World War II that, partly for political and partly for economic reasons, international scientific organisations have proliferated. There are now some sixty inter-governmental, and about three hundred non-governmental scientific organisations. As the scope of these organisations can range from the administration of research establishments, through the co-ordinating and promoting of research projects, to merely the dissemination of research projects, it is difficult to classify them. The most important are listed in Table 12.6 and their methods of action are given in Fig. 12.1. It should be noted that some organisations overlap in their activities. This is usually because of political and economic reasons, which also accounts for the fact that they are largely European.

BIBLIOGRAPHY

COCKCROFT, SIR J. (Ed.), *The Organisation of Research Establishments*, Cambridge University Press (1965)
International Scientific Organisations—1965, Organisation for Economic Co-operation and Development
MELVILLE, SIR H., 'Science Research Council', *Bull. Inst. Phys.*, **17**, p. 3, Jan. (1966)
Technical Services for Industry, Ministry of Technology (1966)
World Space Directory—Spring 1966, American Aviation Publications Inc.
Annual Reports of Government Research Councils and Stations, and Research Associations.
BBC Monographs
The British Imperial Calendar and Civil Service List Annual, H.M.S.O.
U.S. Government Organisation Manual

Chapter 13

Financial Statements and Accounts

It was stated in Chapter 1 that an appreciation of the language of accountants is necessary for the R & D manager. Budgets and costing have been considered earlier, but these are not part of the mechanism of *accounting*, although they are commonly termed *management accounts*, and should be integrated with the accounting system. A further reason for some knowledge is that the published accounts of a company are often the only information a prospective employee can obtain.

It is beyond the scope of this chapter to detail all the accounts and procedures that may be used; only the basic information that may assist in the understanding of a particular system is given.

THE BALANCE SHEET

The balance sheet, the form of which is prescribed by usage rather than law in both the United Kingdom and the United States, has been defined as 'a statement drawn up at the end of each trading or financial period, setting forth the various assets and liabilities of the concern as at this date'.

A balance sheet gives the cumulative financial position of a company since it was registered up to the date given, and shows:

(a) The nature and value of the *assets*
(b) The nature and extent of the *liabilities*
(c) Whether the firm is solvent
(d) Whether the firm is overtrading.

The assets, which are everything the firm owns, must have been purchased; the source of the money is the liabilities, *capital* and *reserves*. To make the balance, a loss must be shown with the assets, whilst unallocated profit will be included in the reserves. If the assets are undervalued, the reserves will be less than they should be, that is there will be *hidden reserves*; but, if the assets are overvalued, they can hide a loss.

If the assets exceed the liabilities the company is solvent by the excess,

193

Table 13.1. THE BALANCE SHEET

BALANCE SHEET As at.................................... 19..........

Liabilities

CREDITORS and ACCRUED CHARGES

e.g. Salaries and wages due ....

Bills payable ....

Bank overdrafts ....

Income tax due ....

Customer advance deposits ....

Provision for workmen's compensation ....

Proposed dividends ....

Debentures and other loans ....

Capital

Preference capital ....

Ordinary capital ....

Reserves

e.g. Capital reserves ....

(Profit) _____

£ ══════

Assets

2/1	Cash in hand	
2/2	Cash at bank	
2/3	Bills receivable	
2/4	Debtors	
2/5	Investments	
2/6	Prepaid rents	
2/7	Insurance premiums (unexpired)	
2/8	Finished goods stock	
2/9	Work in progress	
2/10	Material stocks	
2/11	Office equipment and furniture	
2/12	Loose tools, jigs and fixtures	
2/13	Vehicles	
2/14	Plant and machinery	
2/15	Buildings	
2/16	Land	
2/17	Goodwill	

(Loss) _____

£ ══════

that is the capital and reserves, or *net worth*. It is possible, however, for a firm to be solvent without being sound; this arises if debts are contracted without sufficient means of payment, when the firm is said to be *overtrading*. There must be sufficient liquid assets to pay creditors and provide *working capital*. By liquid assets are meant cash or those assets easily convertible to cash, and it is a common practice to order the assets on the balance sheet according to their fluidity, as shown in Table 13.1.

THE PROFIT AND LOSS ACCOUNT

A more precise designation of *profit and loss account* is the American name *loss and gain account*. Whilst the balance sheet gives the cumulative financial position of a company, the profit and loss account shows the financial results over a period (usually one year). It may be defined as 'an account into which all gains and losses are collected in order to ascertain the excess of the gains over the losses or vice versa. If the gains exceed the losses, the excess is called the net profit; if the losses are greater than the gains, the difference is called the net loss'.

The published profit and loss account, which is a condensed version of the *trading and profit and loss account*, normally only details that information which a company, by law, must disclose.

The trading, and profit and loss accounts may be separate or combined as shown in Table 13.2. It is prepared from a summarised list of the expenditure accounts and income accounts. The trading account may be considered a truncated form of the profit and loss account dealing with direct purchases and manufacturing expenses. On the debit side is included the *stocks* (at true worth) at the commencement of the period, together with the manufacturing expenses incurred during the period; on the credit side is given the sales, and stocks (at true worth) at the end of the period. The *true worth* for finished goods is usually prime costs plus overheads plus part profit; for work in progress, it may only be prime costs plus overheads, and material stock is normally cost. It should be noted that it is this true worth that is transferred to the balance sheet as an asset. The excess of credit over debit in the trading account is the *gross profit*.

THE ACCOUNTANTS' BOOKS

The accountants' books (which may be loose leaf, cards, computer tape), are *journals* and/or *day books*, and *ledgers*. The journals and day books may be likened to diaries in which each and every transaction is recorded before it is entered in the ledgers or accounts. The day books are normally identified by the type of transaction, e.g. purchases, sales, etc., and when an entry is made, a cross reference is given to the relevant account. Entries are made from *vouchers* (invoices, job cards, etc.), each of which is identifiable and kept for reference. The day books are totalled periodically, the total being transferred to a relevant account, for example the periodical total of the purchase day book will be debited to material stocks, and that for the sales day book will be credited to sales.

The terms *debit* and *credit* as used by the accountant differ slightly from normal parlance. This arises from the practice of *double entry*, which is defined as a 'system of book-keeping by means of both personal and impersonal accounts'. Personal accounts are those relating to the

Table 13.2. TRADING AND PROFIT AND LOSS ACCOUNT

Trading and Profit and Loss Account for the Year Ending		19
Opening Work in progress	Sales	
„ Stock		
Direct Labour	Closing work in progress	
„ Purchases	„ stocks	
Gross Profit		
£	£	
Rent and rates	Gross profit b/d	
Indirect wages and salaries	Interest on loans	
Employee insurance and pensions	Interest on investments	
Heating, light and power, etc.	Rents received	
Consumable indirect materials		
Stationery, postage, etc.		
Advertising		
Depreciation		
Directors fees and emoluments		
Interest on loans		
Taxation		
Net profit		
£	£	

persons, companies, etc., with whom the firm deals, that is external accounts; impersonal accounts may be considered as being internal.* In the double entry system, every transaction has a twofold aspect: (a) The yielding of a benefit; (b) The receiving of a benefit.

This yielding and receiving, however, takes place between accounts in the same set of books, the giving being termed 'crediting', and the receiving 'debiting'. The convention of the account format, is to place credits to the right prefacing them by the word 'by', and debits to the left with the word 'to'. The system is illustrated in Table 13.3 which shows a cycle that might occur in an R & D organisation.

The advantages of the double entry system are:

(a) A complete record of every transaction is made, including those involving assets, gains, and losses

---

*Impersonal accounts may be sub-divided into 'real' and 'nominal', the first relating to physical real things, e.g. materials, plant, etc., and nominal accounts being all others, e.g. the profit and loss account heads.

Table 13.3. EXAMPLE OF DOUBLE ENTRY PROCEDURE

(a) Goods received

Dr	Material stock A/C 2/10	Cr
To goods £ 100		

	Creditors A/C 1/4	
	By goods, XYZLM £ 100	

(b) Goods paid

To cash £ 100

	Cash books A/C 2/2	
	By cash £ 100	

(c) Goods issued to project

	Material stock A/C 2/10	
	By goods £ 100	

	Project A/C 2/9	
To goods £ 100		

(d) Direct labour on project

To salaries £ 150

	Cash book A/C 2/2	
	By salaries £ 150	

(e) Project completed

	Project A/C 2/9	
	By contract 250 £	

	Contracts (prime costs) A/C 3/20	
To contract £ 250		

(f) Project invoiced (overheads and profits added to A/C 3/20)

	Sales A/C 4/1	
	By sales £ ABC Limited 750	

(continued overleaf)

Table 13.3 *continued*

Debtors A/C 2/4
£ To ABC Limited 750

(g) Project paid

£
By ABC Limited 750

Cash book A/C 2/2
To cash   £ ABC Limited   750

(h) Trial balance—this can be done at any stage

	£			£
DEBITS TOTAL	2450		CREDITS TOTAL	2450

(b) Full information concerning the business is furnished by the complete record made through the impersonal accounts
(c) A check is kept on arithmetical accuracy. Since every credit has a corresponding debit, the totals must be equal, and this is ascertained by making a *trial balance*
(d) The balance sheet and profit and loss account can be prepared directly from the books.

ACCOUNTING FOR R & D EXPENDITURE

R & D expenditure may either be treated as a job, written off, or as an investment. If the purpose of the work has an end product for which sales may be forecast, then the expenditure can be treated as an investment. This cannot always be done, for example, when feasibility and design studies are concerned, or when the work is in the nature of a long term general development, the only practical solution is for the expenditure to be written off. This means that the expenditure may be recovered totally or partially as an overhead charge, or funded from the net profit after taxation depending on what is allowed by the tax authorities. If the work is done under contract, or in industry is chargeable to a division of the company, it will naturally be considered a job.

BIBLIOGRAPHY

TAINSH, J. A. R., *The Key to Accounting and Costing*, Charles Griffin (1959)
GARBUTT, D., *Advanced Accounts, Carter's*, 5th edit., Pitman (1962)

198

Glossary of Terms

ADMINISTRATION

ADMINISTRATION   The process of interpreting policy and translating it into executive action.

ANALYSIS   The 'resolution of anything complex into its simple elements; the exact determination of its components'.
  ANALYSIS OF WORK   the resolution of a job of work into its component parts, that is, tasks, activities and work packages. It is preliminary to preparing the plan of work.
  NETWORK ANALYSIS (q.v.)   the representation of the plan of work in the form of a diagram, to indicate the sequence of work packages or activities.
  JOB ANALYSIS   the resolution of a job into its prescribed and discretionary components, together with the mechanisms used to review the way in which discretion is exercised.
  COST ANALYSIS   the resolution of the cost of either whole or part of a project into various areas of prime costs and overheads, to determine how expenditure has arisen, and to ascertain whether it has been properly incurred.
  SYSTEMS ANALYSIS   with any information system it is essential to find out exactly who wants the information, when it is required, why, and in what form. Such an analysis is preparatory to a computer programme.

AUTHORITY   The property attaching to a role which enables the person holding the job to undertake his activities, e.g. utilise resources. The degree of authority must be consistent with the degree of responsibility.

CENTRALISATION   A policy which deprives the immediate subordinates of a director, or manager, of their use of discretion in a decreed matter or matters; in contrast:
  DE-CENTRALISATION   the director or manager sets a policy allowing his immediate subordinates to use discretion.

COLLATERAL RELATIONSHIP   The relationship which obtains between colleagues when their work is interdependent.

COMMAND   The *extended* command of a manager comprises all the staff under his control. His *immediate* command is that staff grouping which is directly responsible to him.

CONJOINT RELATIONSHIP   The relationship which exists between specialists responsible to the same manager.

CONTRACTION   The situation which obtains when the executive chain is contracted, i.e. when a manager makes contact with a member of his staff who is not under his immediate command.

DECISION THEORY   A technique for helping to make decisions under conditions of uncertainty and risk. Given the criteria selected by the decision maker, Decision Theory points to the best possible course, irrespective of whether the forecasts are accurate or not.

DEPARTMENT   The specialist commands within a company or division of a company, e.g. sales, accounts.

DIRECTIVE   Written instructions given by a director to his immediate subordinates, which will have long term standing.

DISCRETION   This is the authority to decide or to act according to one's own judgement.

DIVISION   Operational commands within a company which may function independently of other divisions, e.g. independent product organisations.

INNOVATION   The technical, industrial and commercial steps which lead to the marketing of new manufactured products, and to the commercial use of new technical processes and equipment.

INSTRUCTION   Any communication from a superior to one or more of his subordinates when they are in their executive roles. This definition includes not only orders, but also requests for information, etc., which always contain, either explicity or implicity, an instruction.

POLICY INSTRUCTION   a communication from a manager to any or all of his subordinates, stating the policies which they must observe. Policy statements define the boundaries within which a subordinate will be expected to exercise his own judgement, and the aims to which he must orientate his decisions. A project authorisation may be considered a policy instruction.

ACTIVITY (JOB) INSTRUCTION   an activity instruction is a communication from a manager to a subordinate giving him a specific job of work. Activity (job) instructions are, by definition, always given within the framework of policy already set.

STAFF INSTRUCTION   an instruction given by a staff officer, within his own manager's policy, to any of that manager's immediate subordinates.

LINE INSTRUCTION   an instruction given by a member of the staff, within his own manager's policy, to any of his own immediate subordinates.

TECHNICAL INSTRUCTION   an instruction given by a member of the staff, within his own manager's policy, to another member of the staff who is not his immediate subordinate. It is similar to a staff instruction, except that it is confined to communicating technical information, to enable the subordinate to perform satisfactorily those duties for which he is responsible to his own superior.

200

INTERFACE The boundary between two interdependent organisations, or parts of an organisation, defined by their areas of responsibility and/or specialist functions. A 'good interface relationship' arises when there is mutual understanding.

LEGISLATION The process of deciding the policy within which executive action will take place.

MANAGEMENT BY EXCEPTION A report is made to the management if, and only if, something exceptional has happened; this obviates the necessity of investigating work which is going according to plan.

MARKETING Those business activities devoted to:
1. Identifying specific markets for products and services
2. Identifying existing and future needs and wants of these markets
3. Guiding the development of products, packages and services to fill these needs at a profit
4. Selling, delivering, collecting for, and effecting legal transfer (or rights to the use) of these goods and services to the ultimate consumer or user.

ORDER This term may be used as a synonym for INSTRUCTION, whilst implying an immediate response and no exercise of discretion.
STANDING ORDER this refers to instructions from the manager applicable in defined circumstances to all staff.
ORDER may also be used in the contractual sense; for obtaining goods or services.

ORGANISATION The selection, arrangement and use of men, equipment and materials which are suitable for a particular function, e.g. research, production.

ORGANISATION AND METHODS (O & M) A study of the best form of organisation and the clerical (in the broadest sense) methods to be used in a business. It is concerned with Systems Analysis (q.v.) office equipment, printing, copying and duplicating, typing services, office layout, etc. By appropriate study of methods and laying down standards of performance (sometimes allied to incentives) for clerical work, it is often possible to make substantial savings.

PLANNING, CORPORATE Approach to top level management problems emphasising:
1. The need for the company to decide exactly its objectives
2. The need for long range planning in every part of the company to achieve these objectives.
Highly systematic versions of this approach are beginning to appear.

POLICY A statement of the aims, objectives, or targets which are to be achieved, and the methods which are to be used. Policy may be considered as the limits for exercise of discretion.
COMPANY POLICY refers to the policy circumscribing the whole company, in the sense of the extended command of the managing director or president.
DEFINITIVE POLICY that which circumscribes the activities of the board of directors.

RESOURCES The availability of finance, particular skills or materials.
RESOURCE ALLOCATION the planning of manpower and facilities for optimum effectiveness.

RESPONSIBILITY   The obligation on a person to do the work allocated to him.

TECHNIQUE   The method or methods by which any particular activity is carried out.

WORK   The totality of discretion which a member of the staff is expected to exercise, and the prescribed acts he must discharge in carrying out the responsibilities of the role which he occupies.

DISCRETIONARY ACT   an act or course of action adopted by a member of the staff in doing his work, where the policy set for him leaves alternative courses of action, from among which he has to choose.

PRESCRIBED ACT   an act or course of action performed by a member of the staff in doing his work, where the policy set for him allows him no choice.

CONTRACTS

AGREEMENT   A manifestation of mutual assent between two or more enterprises (or persons).

BINDING   an agreement which can be enforced legally.

NON-BINDING   an agreement whose observance rests upon something other than force of law.

EXPLICIT   an agreement which is manifested in words (oral or written).

IMPLICIT   an agreement which is merely inferred from the conduct of the parties.

BREAK CLAUSE   The provision in a contract which provides for its termination before the completion of its full term, either after a specified interval or intervals, or upon the happening of certain events, by one party giving notice to the other in the manner provided in the contract.

CEILING PRICE   Applies to certain United Kingdom Government Contracts. It is a maximum price which, after cost investigation, is liable to be reduced while allowing a reasonable margin of profit, but can never be increased.

COMMERCIAL EXPLOITATION   Commercial use by contractors of designs, or of jigs, tools, etc. provided wholly or partly at Government expense. 'Commercial use' may include manufacture of equipment for other than Crown use, by the granting of licences by the Government contractor to other firms for manufacture to the design.

LEVY   sums payable to the Government by contractors (normally an agreed percentage of the contractor's receipts) in respect of the commercial exploitation of design, jigs and tools, etc.

RIGHTS   the right contained in an agreement with a Government Department to exploit commercially a product previously produced or developed for that Government Department subject to the payment of an agreed sum by way of royalties or fees.

COMPANY   The legal entity comprising Stock or Shareholders and the Board of Directors.

CONCESSION   Permission to utilise a limited quantity of material, parts, components or articles which do not conform strictly to the specification, drawing or pattern, and is intended to cover only a particular batch of material, parts, components or articles already manufactured.

CONDITION A material term or provision in a contract; failure to observe this by one party entitles the other party to treat the contract as repudiated, and gives rights of action for breach of contract.

STANDARD CONDITIONS OF CONTRACT (COMPANY) conditions upon which all orders are placed or accepted in the absence of any indication to the contrary. They are usually printed on the reverse of official order and confirmation of order forms.

'STANDARD CONDITIONS OF GOVERNMENT CONTRACTS FOR STORES PURPOSES (UNITED KINGDOM)' a booklet of conditions adopted by the principal Government Departments (including the Post Office) for the purpose of ensuring uniformity of contract conditions with suppliers. The booklet is published by H.M.S.O. under reference F.CCC/Stores/1. Different forms of conditions apply to the Ministry of Defence (Navy Department) and the United Kingdom Atomic Energy Authority.

CONSIDERATION One of the vital elements of a valid contract. It implies the passing of something of value in exchange for goods or services.

CONTRACT An agreement for supply of goods, or performance of work, at a price agreed or to be agreed. A contract comes into existence when one party makes an offer to another party which that party expressly or by implication accepts unconditionally. Thus, if a quotation is submitted setting out all the main terms, and is accepted by the other party, a binding contract comes into existence. If an acceptance is not unconditional then such acceptance is likely to be a counter offer and the contract does not come into existence unless it is in turn accepted by the first party.

DETERMINATION OF CONTRACT the termination of a contract before the requirements of the contract have been discharged fully, either by invoking contract conditions under which one of the parties has the power to terminate, or by negotiation between the two parties.

DEVELOPMENT CONTRACT a contract covering the development of specified equipment to a required standard.

FIXED PRICE CONTRACT a contract resulting from a tender action, or an ITP, or a Local Purchase Order, where the price has been agreed; the price may be revised only to take into account any amendments or modifications to the contract.

HOLDING CONTRACT a contract placed in order to avoid disbandonment of the team built up by a contractor during a project study, and to maintain the momentum of promising projects pending a decision on whether to proceed with development.

INCENTIVE DEVELOPMENT CONTRACT (Incentive Contract)—a contract containing some provision intended to give an incentive to the contractor to exercise efficiency and economy in time/effort/control of expenditure (e.g., a fixed price, a maximum price, a fixed sum for profit).

RESEARCH AND DEVELOPMENT CONTRACTS, GOVERNMENT these cover that part of R & D work not undertaken in Government establishments. The type of work ranges from fundamental research into basic problems at one end of the scale, to the development of already proved prototypes into production models, at the other end.

RUNNING CONTRACTS agreements whereby a contractor undertakes during a stated period to supply stated articles at stated prices on demand.

DESIGN AUTHORITY A design organisation to whom is delegated full responsibility for evolving designs of equipments or of parts thereof which will satisfy all the requirements of the technical specifications for such equipments or parts issued by a Government Department, and for certifying accordingly.

DESIGN RIGHTS Design rights comprise property in the results of development work and may extend to rights in patents and registered designs and copyright in drawings, reports, specifications, etc.

HANDOVER The formal transfer of ownership of an equipment or system.

GOVERNMENT SUB-CONTRACT ENQUIRY A document emanating from a main Government contractor, setting out the detailed requirements in respect of a contract for which a quotation is invited, and specifying *Standard Conditions of Government Contracts.* Such enquiries should include a Government Contract Number.

INSTRUCTIONS TO PROCEED (ITP) A document issued by a Government Department to a particular firm in advance of the normal contract procedure. It is a firm contract in all respects except that of price, which has to be agreed at a later date.

LIMITATION OF LIABILITY A figure inserted in R & D contracts, other than those placed at fixed or maximum prices, to specify the limit beyond which the Department will not meet the contractor's costs (including profit). The Limitation of Liability may be subject to adjustment in the course of the contract.

LOAN
  CONTRACT LOAN issue of stores and equipment without charge on which the contractor will work under the terms of a contract normally returning the equipment at the conclusion of the contract in a modified or refurbished condition.
  EMBODIMENT LOAN stores issued without charge to a contractor specifically for incorporation in equipment being manufactured, repaired or developed in accordance with a Government contract.
  ORDINARY LOAN issue of equipment without charge for a particular purpose and for a specific period at the end of which the item is intended to be returned unchanged in condition except for fair wear and tear.
  REPAYMENT LOAN an issue under conditions imposing a charge to be collected from the contractor either at stated intervals or on eventual return of the equipment.
  DEFERRED REPAYMENT LOAN an issue in accordance with contract terms which provide for financial recovery by deduction from the contractor's bills in respect of the articles delivered.

LOCAL PURCHASE ORDER A contract placed other than by a Government Contracts Division under authority delegated. The system is subject to individual monetary limits and to the instructions set out.

PATENT INDEMNITY Provision in a contract whereby the company is required to accept responsibility for inadvertent infringement of Letters Patent or Registered Designs arising out of use or sale of goods.

PENALTY CLAUSE Contractual provision whereby a seller is committed to pay a previously agreed sum as damages for failure to supply goods to the required specification and/or on the date provided in the contract.

PRICE VARIATION   A provision made in a quoted price to cover future increases in costs. The areas of such increases should be defined, e.g. wage demands, either national or local, or other variations anticipated if production extends over a number of years.

PROGRESS PAYMENT   A provision in a contract whereby payment is made at stated intervals usually to certain limits based on costs incurred as work proceeds; or whereby an agreed payment is made, which is later offset against the price agreed finally.

PROPRIETARY ARTICLE   This may be regarded as an article made to a design in respect of which the parent firm has a prima facie claim to remuneration if the design is used by a Government Department through other contractors. Such claims do not depend necessarily on patents or registered designs, but may derive from the expenditure, work and skill of the firm.

QUOTATION   An offer made to a customer to supply goods at certain prices; in the absence of precise words indicating that the quotation is not an offer it will, if accepted by the customer within the time specified, give rise to a firm contract.

SPECIAL PLANT   Plant which has to be installed especially for the purpose of carrying out a contract or manufacture of a product and which is not likely to have any substantial application to other contracts or products.

SPECIAL PRODUCTS   Those materials, components or assemblies which are basically to a customer's design or specification.

TECHNICAL COST INVESTIGATION (UNITED KINGDOM)   An investigation by Government Technical Cost Officers, in conjunction with officers of the company, to establish a basis for price negotiation with the relevant Government Contracts Department.

TENDER   A formal offer submitted by the company, generally to a Government Department, in which the company makes a quotation on terms specified in the tender. Upon acceptance by the customer it becomes binding on the company.
   SINGLE ACTION TENDER   a tender for which one company only has been asked to quote.
   INVITATION TO TENDER   a document which emanates from a Government Department, National Authority, or similar body usually on an official printed form, setting out in detail the requirements in respect of a contract for which quotations are invited.

WARRANTY   A guarantee given by the company for the rectification or replacement of faulty goods under specified conditions. A contingency is normally included in the price to cover anticipated costs.

COSTS AND ESTIMATES

BUDGET   A financial and/or quantitative statement, prepared and approved prior to a defined period of time, of the policy to be pursued during that period for the

205

purpose of attaining a given objective. It may include income, expenditure, and the employment of capital.

FUNCTIONAL (EXPENDITURE) BUDGET a budget of income or expenditure appropriate to, or the responsibility of, a particular function.

BUDGETARY CONTROL   The establishment of budgets relating to the responsibilities of executives to the requirements of a policy, and the continuous comparison of actual with budgeted results either to secure by individual action the objective of that policy or to provide a basis for its revision.

CARRIAGE   The cost of transporting goods from a despatch point to the delivery point specified by or on behalf of the customer. For goods supplied 'ex-works', carriage is charged separately. If 'carriage paid', the cost should be included in the price build-up.

CONTINGENCY   An element in a price build-up intended to cover expenses liable to be incurred in the execution of the contract which are not covered under the normal heads of expense. This also covers a margin where known facts for the elements of expenditure, which have been included in the estimate, are not considered reliable.

COST
  1. The amount of expenditure (actual or notional) incurred on, or attributable to, a given thing.
  2. To ascertain the amount of expenditure for a given thing.
The word 'cost' can rarely stand on its own and should be qualified as to its nature or limitations (e.g. historical, variable, etc.) and related to a particular thing or 'object of thought' (e.g. a given quantity or unit of goods made or services performed).
  ELEMENTS OF COST   the primary classification of costs according to the factors upon which expenditure is incurred:
    MATERIALS COST   the cost of commodities supplied to an undertaking.
    WAGES (LABOUR COST)   the cost of remuneration of employees.
    EXPENSES   the cost of services provided to an undertaking, and the notional cost of the use of owned assets.
  CLASSIFICATION OF COSTS:
    PRODUCTION (WORKS) COST   the cost of the sequence of operations which begins with supplying materials, labour, and services, and ends with primary packing of the product.
    ADMINISTRATION COST   the cost of formulating the policy, directing the organisation and controlling the operations of an undertaking, which is not related directly to a production, selling, distribution, research or development activity or function, each of which should have its own cost.
  TOTAL COST   the sum of all costs attributable to the unit under consideration, i.e. production cost, administration and other costs, recovery factors, royalties and discounts, and contingencies. To the TOTAL COST is added PROFITS and SALES REBATES to arrive at the SELLING PRICE.
  PRIME COST   The aggregate of direct costs, that is costs which can be identified with, and allocated cost centres or cost units. These direct costs are:
    DIRECT MATERIALS COST
    DIRECT WAGES (direct labour cost)
    DIRECT EXPENSES
These costs are usually VARIABLE, in that they tend to vary directly with volume of output, although some may be FIXED, and do not vary with the output.

COST BUDGET Estimation of expenditure to be incurred in the completion of individual projects, or in the completion of technically defined phases, or units of project or research work.

COST CENTRE A location, person, or item of equipment for which costs may be ascertained, and used for the purposes of cost control.

COST UNIT A unit of quantity of product, service, (or time for a combination of these) in relation to which costs may be ascertained or expressed, e.g.
    JOB a single order or contract
    BATCH a group of identical items
    PRODUCT a group of similar products.

DEVELOPMENT COST PLAN (D.C.P.) A statement made before the development stages of a project, analysed into areas of effort, the dates by which milestones should be reached, and the cost of reaching them in terms of manpower, money and overall project time. A D.C.P. is used by United Kingdom Government Departments as an instrument of control; further plans may be called for at any time in the life of a project.

ESTIMATE A statement of the planned effort and cost of a particular project from its conception, or some later stage, to completion.
    COST ESTIMATING RELATIONSHIP (C.E.R.) A technique for determining cost on the basis of typical past performance of similar work.

FREE ISSUE ITEMS Items forming part of an assembly which are supplied free by the customer for inclusion in his order. This may include packing. In such cases it is normal to include a contingency to cover handling and wastage.

LAYOUT CHARGES Those charges which are incurred in the physical re-organisation of areas to create a layout or to alter an existing layout. If the charges are capitalised or charged directly to a customer they are termed LAYOUT COSTS, and if not capitalised, that is they are included in production overheads, they are termed LAYOUT EXPENSES.

OVERHEAD The aggregate of indirect costs, that is those costs which cannot be allocated but which can be apportioned to, or absorbed by, cost centres or units. Overheads may be FIXED, in that they tend to be unaffected by variations in the volume of the output, or VARIABLE in that they vary with the volume of the output. Overheads may be classified in the same manner as costs (q.v.), e.g.
    PRODUCTION OVERHEAD
    COMMERCIAL (SELLING, MARKETING) OVERHEAD
    ADMINISTRATION OVERHEAD.

RECOVERY FACTOR A factor included in the price to effect the recovery of a classified cost over a given production run or contract.

ROYALTIES The payments made under covenant for the right to manufacture and sell a particular item. The payee may have financed the development and/or be the owner of a patent.

STOCK HOLDING INTEREST This is an abnormal factor, and for accounting pruposes is dealt with as an extra profit element. It is intended to cover the additional costs involved either for a particular contract or for a particular range of products in stocking materials, components, piece parts or spares for a particular contract or as a service after the main production has been discontinued.

STOCK REDUNDANCY   A loss which arises when materials or piece parts become surplus to foreseeable requirements, or obsolescent due to the customer changing his requirements (technical or quantity), or when they deteriorate because of non-usage.

START-UP   The 'one time' cost of the starting up of production. There will normally be delay in working up to normal efficiency in the case of a new product and any additional cost involved should be included as a direct charge or expense or as an investment recovery factor.

ECONOMICS

DISCOUNTED CASH FLOW   This is the title given to a mathematical technique for deciding the relative advantages of capital investment schemes. It takes into consideration the length of life of an asset and the varying annual cash yield, reducing everything for purposes of comparison to a common base year by year, discounting the future cash returns by the interest earnining capacity of money. See also NET PRESENT VALUE.

LINEAR PROGRAMMING   This is a technique for determining the best mix of products in order to make the most profitable use of the company's manufacturing facilities.

MARKOVITZ PORTFOLIO SELECTION   This takes into account the risk associated with an investment and the risks associated with any investment related to it; for example, if a project to make umbrellas may be risky, so is one to make sunshades —but together the risks are lessened. The problem is to determine the risks.

NET PRESENT VALUE   A rate of return is applied to cash flows, to determine whether their discounted value is greater than the cost of the investment.

PARETO PRINCIPLE   When a particular effect is the result of many different causes, 80% of the observed effect can be accounted for, usually, by only two or three of all the possible causes.

REPLACEMENT THEORY   A body of mathematical and statistical techniques to help decide the optimum life for a particular item of plant. It takes account of second-hand values, increasing repair bills and breakdowns as the plant gets older, tax implications, etc.

TECHNOLOGICAL ADVANCE   The increase in productivity (per man) that cannot be accounted for by the increase in capital invested (per man) according to classical economic theory.

TECHNOLOGICAL FALLOUT (SPILLOVER)   The activities and demands of a particular industry cause increases in the amount of technological knowledge and progress in the fields related to its activity. When these developments can be used to improve the products of another industry, this is known as technological fallout.

INSPECTION AND QUALITY CONTROL

CRITICAL EXAMINATION
1. A detailed dimensional, qualitative and quantitative examination of a selected sample, usually carried out in a test house with equipment not normally available at the manufacturer's works. It may include functional tests if applicable.
2. The examination (usually by an Inspectorate) of newly designed equipment to ascertain the quality of workmanship, components, materials and finish which should be taken into account by the Approving Authority in considering whether or not to approve the design.

INSPECTION   Determination of the quality of materials, components, assemblies, or finished products, for purposes of process control, product control, quality audit, or fault diagnosis.

100% INSPECTION   inspection of each and every unit of product, as opposed to any form of sampling inspection.

DIRECT INSPECTION   When a firm has no approved inspection organisation the Inspectorate carries out its own direct inspection at the firm after the firm has verified compliance with contract requirements.

EXECUTIVE INSPECTION   The actual work of inspection and testing, or the supervision of such work by others.

FINAL INSPECTION   the last of several inspections at successive stages of manufacture, repair, modification, etc.

'NO INSPECTION'   this method of ensuring the correctness of a product places the responsibility on the contractor for certifying that the stores are supplied in accordance with the requirements of the contract. The Advice and Inspection Note is signed by the contractor or his representative and is not certified by an Inspectorate.

NORMAL INSPECTION   inspection which is used when there is no statistically significant evidence that the quality of the product being submitted is better or poorer than the (appropriate) specified quality level.

WAIVED INSPECTION   when it is considered that a store is not of critical importance in a particular application, and when it is considered that the firm's standard of production is sufficiently high for the particular store under consideration, an Inspectorate may decide to waive direct inspection, trusting to the firm's efficiency for the resulting quality. Whenever possible the firm's guarantee is invoked.

INSPECTION BY ATTRIBUTES   inspection wherein certain characteristics of the sample units are inspected and classified simply as conforming, or not conforming, to specified requirements. If desired, the degree of non-conformance may be further categorised through the use of such classifications as critical, major or minor.

INSPECTION BY VARIABLES   inspection wherein certain characteristics of the sample units are evaluated with respect to a numerical scale and are expressed as precise points along this scale. The distribution of these points, as established by measures of their central tendency and dispersion, are mathematically related to specified requirements to determine the degree of conformance of these characteristics.

LINE INSPECTION   in-process inspection, i.e., inspection of an item at one of the intermediate stages of its production process as distinct from final inspection (q.v.) or inspection for other nominated purposes.

ON-RECEIPT (RECEIVING) INSPECTION   inspection by a consumer of material and manufactured products as delivered to him.

REDUCED INSPECTION   provision in a sampling procedure for switching to a less severe sampling plan when average quality offered is high.

SAMPLING INSPECTION   evaluation of the quality of material or units of a product

209

by the inspection of samples, as distinct from 100 per cent inspection.

TIGHTENED INSPECTION   provision in a sampling procedure for swtcihing to a more severe sampling plan when average quality offered is poor.

INSPECTING AUTHORITY   The authority responsible for ensuring that items are manufactured and delivered in accordance with the terms of the contract.

INSPECTORATE (PRIME)   The Inspectorate (Government) ultimately responsible for a complete store or equipment; it is the Inspectorate named as the inspection authority in a contract.

MEAN TIME BETWEEN FAILURES (MTBF)   A term used in defining the reliability of equipment. It is the ratio of the number of hours of operating time during the normal operating life of the equipment, to the number of failures experienced in that time. Normal operating life is the period, when failures are random and independent, between the early period of higher failure rate (e.g. due to manufacturing faults), and the period where higher failure rates are due to wear of some of the parts concerned.

OPERATOR CONTROL   That part of process control which is carried out by the operator.

PERFORMANCE   The manner or success in working of a product or service.

PROCESS CAPABILITY   The limits of inherent variability within which a machine tool or other process can operate.

PROCESS CONTROL   That part of quality control concerned with minimising variations in quality level which occur during the production process.

QUALITY: (FITNESS FOR PURPOSE)   The degree to which a product or service meets the requirements of the customer. With manufactured products, quality is a combination of quality of design and quality of manufacture.
  QUALITY ASSESSMENT   the determination of the quality of a product or service by examination, testing and experiment.
  QUALITY ASSURANCE   the provision of evidence or proof that contractual requirements for quality have been met. In a manufacturing company this function usually includes the overall supervision of the quality control system.
  QUALITY AUDIT   the monitoring of quality levels at any stage to provide information for management.
  QUALITY CONTROL   a management system for programming and co-ordinating the quality maintenance and improvement efforts of the various groups in a design and/or manufacturing organisation, so as to enable production at the most economic levels allowing for full customer satisfaction.
  QUALITY CONTROL SURVEILLANCE   supervision by the customer or his representative of a contractor's quality control organisation and methods.
  QUALITY OF DESIGN   the value inherent in the design; a measure of the excellence of the design in relation to the customer's requirements.
  QUALITY ENGINEERING   the application of specialised managerial, scientific and technological skills to achieve the desired quality at minimum cost.
  QUALITY OF MANUFACTURE: (QUALITY OF CONFORMANCE)   a measure of the fidelity with which the product taken at the point of acceptance conforms to the design.

210

PROFESSIONAL QUALITY the standard of quality and reliability similar to that specified for government supplies.

QUALITY CONTROL, STATISTICAL A number of statistical methods have been developed to aid in checking and controlling the quality of manufactured goods, or checking that goods received are up to the specification on which they were bought. The general aim of these techniques is to balance the cost of inspection against the penalties of allowing faulty materials to escape detection. Thus total cost is minimised.

ACCEPTABLE QUALITY LEVEL (AQL) the maximum per cent defective (or maximum number of defects per 100 units) that, for the purpose of sampling inspection, can be considered acceptable as a true process average.

CONFIDENCE LEVEL the probability that the true value estimated, for example, from a number of differing test results, lies within certain limits (confidence limits). Thus, confidence level refers to the degree of assurance provided by the test results that a specified requirement has been met.

CONTROL CHART A chart, with upper and/or lower control limits, on which are plotted values of some statistical measure for a series of samples or sub-groups. The chart frequently shows a central line to assist detection of a trend of plotted values towards either control limit.

LOT TOLERANCE PER CENT DEFECTIVE (LTPD) the incoming fraction defective (or numbers of defects per 100 units) that the consumer is willing to accept with a very small probability of occurrence, (q.v. acceptable quality level: consumer's risk.)

PROCESS AVERAGE when the quality level of a unit of product can be specified by a single measurement, the mean of the population of such measurements produced by a process is known as the process average. It is usually impractical to find this value directly and hence it is estimated from results of examinations of samples.

RELIABILITY The measure of the ability of a product to function successfully, when required, for the period required, in the specific environment. It is expressed as a probability.

INHERENT RELIABILITY the reliability potential present in a design, i.e., the theoretical reliability which is dependent solely on the quality of design and assumes perfect quality of manufacture and correct use in the field.

ACHIEVED RELIABILITY the reliability demonstrated at a given point in time under specified conditions of use and environment.

RISK, CONSUMER'S The probability that a batch of goods will be accepted by a sampling plan as a result of a satisfactory sample being drawn from an unsatisfactory batch.

RISK, PRODUCER'S The probability that a batch of goods will be rejected by a sampling plan as a result of an unsatisfactory sample being drawn from a satisfactory batch.

SAMPLE A sample is one or more units of product taken from a batch, or a portion of material taken from a bulk quantity in order to represent that batch or bulk quantity for inspection purposes.

SAMPLING PLAN The specification of the rules to be followed in sampling inspection in sentencing any particular batch of articles.

SEQUENTIAL ANALYSIS Allows one to determine whether sufficient accuracy has been achieved from the samples already taken, or whether a further sample should be taken.

TECHNICAL DIRECTION The promulgation of instructions detailing the inspection and testing required for a technique, store, contract or order and the continuing technical support to executive inspection as deemed necessary by the Inspectorate.

TYPE (OR QUALIFICATION) APPROVAL Type approval is given by an Approving Authority to articles, usually of a proprietary nature, which have passed to the Authority's satisfaction, the tests and other requirements of a performance speci-fication which is not necessarily a full manufacturing specification for the article concerned.
(*Note:* In some fields, notably that of active and passive electronic components, the term Qualification Approval is used instead of Type Approval.)
MAINTENANCE OF TYPE APPROVAL (MTA) MTA covers the submission of type approval items at regular intervals for testing, to ensure that the original standard is maintained. The incidence of submission is governed by the terms of the relevant specification, or may be called for at the discretion of the inspection authority.

ZERO DEFECTS Places the emphasis on making an item correct first time, i.e., to the drawing or specification as applicable, rather than to removing the faulty items by examination or inspection. The purpose of a Zero Defects Programme is to persuade people to accept the challenge of doing their job right first time.

RESEARCH AND DEVELOPMENT

DESIGN
1. The process whereby existing information, data and techniques are applied in evolving an item to be manufactured to meet a specific requirement.
2. A general term for the product of the design process, with specific reference to stage of development, status, or means of description or portrayal.

DEVELOPMENT The stage between research and the production of equipment. It may be regarded, generally, as the sequel to applied research, and the boundary between them is not always clear cut. However, development normally involves the application of known scientific techniques and processes to projects whose technical feasibility has been established.

RESEARCH The endeavour to discover facts by scientific study involving a course of critical examination. The first stage in the evolution of a new product falls into the following categories:
BASIC RESEARCH research directed towards the increase of scientific knowledge.
EXPLORATORY RESEARCH the detailed examination of a particular phenomenon to establish its technological requirements in order to find a way of satisfying such requirements.
CONCEPT ANALYSIS the preliminary study of the engineering consequences of an idea for the creation of new, or the adaption of an existing technique, product or equipment.
APPLIED RESEARCH research which has as its objective the attaining of a practical goal which can be defined, such as a new process or piece of equipment.

SERVICE An activity carried out by a member of the staff at the request of another, not in the same line of command, which it is his executive responsibility to perform for others.

R & D SERVICES or engineering services, cover the work carried out by R & D or engineering personnel ancillary to the production and sales operations, and include the efforts entailed in ensuring that:

1. production proceeds in the most efficient manner
2. the sales operation is given technical assistance in obtaining business
3. the customer receives such technical help and guidance after delivery as is necessary to enable him to utilise the goods in a satisfactory way.

POST DESIGN SERVICE the service provided by a nominated authority after an equipment has been introduced into use. This authority normally assumes the role of the design authority in respect of the equipment and is responsible for the maintenance of design and manufacturing data, the investigation of user defect reports and the initiation of any modification action which may result therefrom.

GENERAL TERMS

AMENDMENT (OF DRAWINGS AND SPECIFICATIONS) A change is categorised as an amendment when its effect is to eliminate drawing errors, make minor manufacturing changes or bring design records into line with manufacturing practices without affecting any of the criteria which cause a change to be categorised as a modification.

APPROVAL
DESIGN APPROVAL the approval given to a development project by the design authority, testifying that the design specification has been met.
TYPE APPROVAL this approval follows when the item is in production, and has been shown to meet all service requirements.

ASSESSMENT REPORT A survey of the advantages which would accrue if the project were approved, and of the effort and knowledge which would be required to achieve them.

DESIGN APPROVED FIRM A firm whose senior design staff, design and development organisation testing and other facilities have been approved in respect of a defined field of activities.

DEVELOPMENT AIM A statement of the characteristics which an equipment or system should possess when it has been designed and developed to satisfy an appropriate requirement.

DEVELOPMENT BATCH A batch of early production standard equipment manufactured on a contract initiated by the developing authority.

DRAWINGS, DESIGN Drawings to an acceptable standard, delineating the design as it is at any given stage in development.

DRAWINGS, MASTER That drawing which is accepted by the responsible authority as the ultimate reference.

ERGONOMICS The anatomical, physiological and psychological study of man in

213

his working environment with the aim of fitting equipment to the worker.

FEASIBILITY STUDY   A study undertaken to identify the scientific and technical problems involved in meeting a requirement, and to assess whether they can be solved. Normally it will not involve any experimental work or engineering, but should include approximate indications of the cost and time that would be necessary to complete the project.

INFORMATION RETRIEVAL   The selection of documentary information of a defined subject by means of a literature search.

INTERCHANGEABILITY   An interchangeable part is one so designed and manufactured that, under any combination of dimensions and tolerances permitted by the drawings and of performance permitted by the test specifications, it will, without alteration and within the range of adjustment provided, assemble with its mating part or parts, and perform its operational function within the specification limits for the assembly.

LOGISTICS   The support of all types of operations (usually military) including:
TRANSPORTATION   by sea, land and air
DEPLOYMENT   and re-supply of resources
MAINTENANCE   of all forms of equipment including servicing repair and replacement, and provision of information therefore
MANNING   of logistic installations, units and bases.

MILESTONES   Intermediate objectives within the overall objective as defined in a development plan.

MODEL
EXPERIMENTAL   A model constructed in order to determine how the assumptions made in design will work out in practice, or to explore particular areas of uncertainty.
MOCK-UP   A scale model, either whole or part, generally full size, usually not working, to ascertain suitability of arrangement.
PATTERN   A model used as a standard to which all subsequent models must conform.
SEALED PATTERN   A pattern whose design cannot be changed except in accordance with agreed modification procedure and by agreement with the customer.
PILOT MODEL   The first full scale working model constructed to production or manufacturing drawings to prove such drawings.
PROTOTYPE   The first model subjected to tests and on which all subsequent models are based. A prototype is not necessarily produced by the technique which will be used for production in quantity.

MODIFICATION   Any design change which affects one or more of the following criteria:
1. Safety, operational use or other specified requirement
2. Cost or delivery date
3. Interchangeability
4. The service identification of any item already being manufactured or which has been delivered
5. Special tools or special to type equipment
6. Involves retrospective embodiment on equipments already delivered or which will be delivered before the design change takes effect in production.

214

OPERATIONAL RESEARCH   The application of scientific processes to operational problems arising within organisations, the objective being to make more effective use of known facts, to enlarge the proportion of factual knowledge and to reduce the proportion of subjective judgement in making management decisions.

PACKAGING   The art of, and the operations involved in, the preparation of supplies for carriage, storage and delivery to the consumer. The term embraces preservation, identification and packing.

PROJECT   A project encompasses, generally, the whole body of design, development, and testing work, both intra- and extra-mural, which is involved in meeting a requirement, and the applied research associated with it.
> PROJECT STUDY   a detailed examination of the scientific and technical problems involved in developing equipment to meet a requirement, leading up to a plan of design, development and testing (quantified in terms of money, manpower and time) and to an indication of subsequent production costs.

PUBLICATION
> DOCUMENTARY   indicates availability to the public without restriction, generally by sales.
> PATENTS   indicates availability of information to the public.

RIG   A test frame on which the functioning of any separate part of an equipment or system can be examined and/or tested under chosen environmental conditions.

SEALING OF DESIGN   Acceptance that drawings are suitable for release for manufacturing purposes in quantity production and that equipment manufactured to such drawings will be acceptable to the customer.
After sealing has been effected, the design authority responsible for such drawings is only permitted to make design changes in accordance with agreed modification procedure, and by agreement with the customer.

SPECIAL TO TYPE EQUIPMENT   Ancillary equipment designed specially for use with a particular major equipment.

SPECIFICATION   A clear and accurate series of statements of the technical requirements for an article or service; each statement should consist of these elements:
1. The characteristic, e.g. dimensions, performance
2. The limit for the characteristic, which may be quantitative or qualitative
3. The method of test or assessment.
A design specification states the overall technical results which are required in the production article; a test specification states the test procedures which will be used to establish whether the design specification has been complied with; a manufacturing or production specification states production technique requirements.

STANDARDISATION   Standards may be divided broadly into:
1. DESIGN STANDARDS   specifying performance and functional requirements
2. PHYSICAL STANDARDS   specifying dimensional requirements, geometry of attachments, or actual design or parts to be used.

SYSTEM   A collection of items between which exists connection, relation and interaction and which together form a unity for the achievement of a specific purpose.
> SYSTEMS ANALYSIS   the postulation, study and evaluation of alternative systems to achieve an operational objective.

215

TEST   A procedure to enable a qualitative/quantitative assessment of a particular characteristic of the item being tested, under specified controlled conditions which are repeatable.

TRIAL   A qualitative/quantitative assessment of all or some of the characteristics and performance of the item being tested, under actual operational conditions or conditions simulating those likely to be met.

   TRIAL INSTALLATION   the incorporation and testing of a specimen equipment or specimen part of equipment in an aircraft, guided weapon, radar, etc., to find out whether the design of the installation is satisfactory.

USER TRIAL   trials carried out by the user's own personnel to satisfy the user that equipments are suitable for acceptance.

VALUE ENGINEERING   An organised effort at the design stage directed at analysing the function of systems, equipment and components with the purpose of achieving the required function at the lowest overall cost, consistent with requirements for performance, reliability and maintainability.

NETWORK ANALYSIS

TECHNIQUES

BRANCHING NETWORK   There will sometimes be several ways of completing a project. But until it has progressed to a certain point, it cannot be decided which way it should be completed. Branching networks can be used in these cases.

CRITICAL PATH METHOD (C.P.M.)   A management technique based upon charting as a network the inter-relationship between events leading to the desired objective, and placing a time value on the activities necessary to accomplish the events, so that the longest (critical) path through the network to the objective is identified. Monitoring progress of the activities on this critical path ensures timely completion of a project, since any changes in activity times along the path automatically affect the duration of the project.

DECISION TREES   Managers are very often faced with not one decision, but a whole network extending into the future. Displaying these as a branching tree diagram in which the probabilities of the outcomes of each decision are shown can help to evaluate the best immediate choice.

PERT   An acronym for PROJECT EVALUATION AND REVIEW TECHNIQUE which in its broad sense represents the concept of an integrated management system for planning and controlling the variables of time, cost, and technical performance. It is a variant of the Critical Path Method, used when the variables cannot be forecast accurately.

   PERT/TIME   originally known as PERT, and described in *USAF PERT/TIME System Description Manual*.

   PERT/COST   a technique originally described in *USAF PERT/COST System Description Manual*. It is complementary to the basic PERT/TIME system, in that both cost and schedule are planned and controlled on a common basis by comparisons between estimates and actuals.

   MODULAR CONCEPT PERT/COST   the development and use of separate but compatible data processing programmes for PERT/TIME and PERT/COST, applicable to

216

a common network. The mechanics of data processing in the modular concept involve the sequential processing of the time and cost data.

RESOURCE ALLOCATION   The available resources (men, machines, money, etc.) are so allocated to the various tasks in the project as to minimise the time and/or resources to complete it.

PERT TERMS*

ACTIVITY   An activity is an element of a plan of work which may be:
   a process
   a job to be performed
   a procurement cycle
   waiting time
   an interdependency or constraint between two events.
In a network, an activity is represented by an arrow, and is identified by the precursor and successor events.
   DUMMY ACTIVITY   an activity which does not absorb resources of any kind. It is represented by a dotted arrow, and its function may be either to avoid ambiguity in a network, or to indicate dependencies and controls.
   COST ACTIVITY*   an activity which employs resources, the cost of which is a direct charge to the programme.

CHARGE NUMBER*   A number used for identifying the costs charged to a work package.

CONSTRAINT   The relationship of an event to a succeeding activity wherein the activity may not start until the event preceding it has occurred. The term is also used to indicate the relationship of an activity to a succeeding event wherein an event cannot occur until all activities preceding it have been completed.

COST
ACCELERATED COST   the higher cost rate, which includes the premiums that have to be paid, to perform an activity in a 'crash time'.
   ACTUAL COSTS*   the expenditures incurred plus any pre-specified types of unliquidated commitments charged or assigned to a work effort.
   DIRECT COST*   costs charged directly to the contract.
   COST CATEGORY*   the name and/or number of a functional hardware, or other significant cost category for which costs are to be summarised.
   PLANNED COST*   the approved charge for a work package or summary item. This cost, when totalled with the planned costs for all other work packages, results in the total cost estimate, committed under contract, for the programme or project. 'Planned' and 'budgeted' may be used synonymously.

CRASH TIME   The minimum possible time for completing a project, work package, or activity, without regard to the economic use of resources.

CRITICAL PATH   That particular sequence of activities that has the greatest negative (or least positive) activity slack in a network.

*Terms marked thus throughout this section are applicable to PERT/COST only.

DATE

DIRECTED DATE FOR AN EVENT $(T_D)^*$ date for a specific accomplishment directed by top level authority.

EARLIEST COMPLETION DATE $(S_E)^*$ the S_E value for a given activity is equal to the sum of the scheduled elapsed time (t_s) for the activities on the longest path from the beginning of the programme up to and including the given activity. Thus S_E represents the earliest date on which an activity can be completed.

EARLIEST EXPECTED DATE (T_E) the earliest date for which an event can be expected to occur. The T_E value for a given event is equal to the sum of the statistically calculated expected elapsed times (t_e) for the activities on the longest path from the beginning of the programme to the given event.

LATEST ALLOWABLE DATE (T_L) the latest date on which an event can occur without creating an expected delay in the completion of the programme. The T_L value for a given event is calculated by subtracting the sum of the expected elapsed times (t_e) for the activities on the longest path from the given event to the end of the programme, from the latest date allowable for completing the programme. T_L for the end event in a programme is equal to the directed date (T_D) of the programme. If a directed date is not specified, the T_E for the end event is used as the T_L and recognised as such.

LATEST COMPLETION DATE $(S_L)^*$ the S_L value for a given activity is calculated by subtracting the sum of the scheduled elapsed times (t_s) for the activities on the longest path from the given activity to the end event of the programme from the directed date or latest allowable date (T_L) for completing the programme. S_L therefore represents the latest date on which an activity can be scheduled for completion without delaying the completion of the programme.

SCHEDULED COMPLETION DATE $(T_S)^*$ a date assigned for completion of an activity (accomplishment of an event) for purposes of planning and control within an organisation. Where no specific date is assigned, S_E equals T_S.

ESTIMATE-TO-COMPLETE*   The estimated man-hours, costs and time required to complete a work package or summary item (including applicable overheads except where direct costs are specified).

EVENT   A specific definable accomplishment in a programme plan, recognisable at a particular instant in time. Events do not consume time or resources and are normally represented in the network by circles or rectangles.

PREDECESSOR, BEGINNING or TAIL EVENT   an event which signifies when one or more activities on a network may begin.

SUCCESSOR, END or HEAD EVENT   an event which signifies when one or more activities on a network are completed.

FIRST EVENT NUMBER*   the number of the first event in time (based on S_E) for a work package or summary item. This event number defines the beginning of the work package or summary item in relation to the network.

LAST EVENT NUMBER*   the number of the last event in time (based on S_E) for a work package or summary item. This event number defines the end of the work package or summary item in relation to the network.

FLOAT   This term is used instead of SLACK in C.P.M., although it is not synonymous. It may be specified as:

TOTAL FLOAT   the excess time available when all preceding activities start at the earliest possible times, and all succeeding activities occur at the latest possible times.

FREE FLOAT   the portion of the excess time available when all preceding activities

218

start at the earliest possible time, and all succeeding activities occur at the earliest possible times.

INDEPENDENT FLOAT   the portion of the excess time available when all preceding activities start at the latest possible time, and all succeeding activities occur at the earliest possible times.

ORGANISATION

PERFORMING ORGANISATION*   the contractor or Government organisation which will perform work on a work package.

RESPONSIBLE ORGANISATION*   the contractor or Government organisation responsible for management of a work package.

RESOURCE CODE*   The contractor's code for a particular manpower skill or material type.

SUMMARY ITEM*   An item identified in the work breakdown structure.

SUMMARY LEVEL*   Any level in the work breakdown structure.

SUMMARY NUMBER*   A number which identifies an item in the work breakdown structure.

SLACK

ACTIVITY SLACK   the difference in time, comparing the earliest completion date (S_E) with the latest completion date (S_L) for a given activity. The activity slack indicates the range of time within which an activity can be scheduled for completion. When the S_E for an activity is later than the S_L, then the activity is said to have negative slack and either the current activities or subsequent activities must be replanned or the programme schedule will slip. When S_L for an activity is later than S_E, the activity is said to have positive slack, and additional time is available for performing the activity, without causing the programme schedule to slip. See also FLOAT.

MOST CRITICAL SLACK (WEEKS)   the worst (least algebraic) slack with respect to designated programme or project end points, in weeks, for any of the activities within the work package or summary item. This slack is based on $S_L - S_E$ for each activity. The slack indicated will not necessarily be this difference for the end of a work package or summary item, since the worst slack situation may be associated with an activity within the work package or summary item, rather than at the end of the work package.

STRUCTURE

WORK (PROGRAMME) BREAKDOWN*   a family tree sub-division of a programme, beginning with the end objectives, and then subdividing these objectives into successively smaller end item subdivisions. The programme breakdown structure establishes the framework for:

1. Defining the work to be accomplished
2. Constructing a network plan
3. Summarising the cost and schedule status of a programme for progressively higher levels of management.

ACCOUNT CODE STRUCTURE*   the numbering system used to assign summary numbers to elements of the work breakdown structure and charge numbers to individual work packages.

TIME

SCHEDULED ELAPSED TIME (t_s)* the period of time scheduled for performing an activity.

EXPECTED ELAPSED TIME (t_e) the expected (or statistically computed) time in weeks for accomplishing an activity. The expected elapsed time is identical to a single time estimate for the work to be accomplished or is calculated using the formula:

$$\frac{a+4m+b}{6} = t_e$$

WORK PACKAGE* The unit of work required to complete a specific job or process, such as a report, a design, a documentation requirement, a piece of hardware or a service. A work package may consist of one or more cost significant activities. The content of a work package may be limited to the work which can be performed by a single operating unit in an organisation or may require the contributing services of several operating units. The overall responsibility for the work content of a work package should be assigned to a single organisation or responsible individual.

PERSONNEL

INCENTIVE SCHEMES Modern version of 'piecework' or payment by results. In its best form some part of a man's pay will depend on the work he puts into his job as measured by time study or by other techniques.

INTELLIGENCE, PERSONALITY AND APTITUDE TESTS Intelligence tests are a good guide to some sorts of intelligence but must be supplemented by an interviewer's personal assessment. Personality tests are still very suspect, although they may uncover otherwise unsuspected traits. Aptitude tests may be a useful guide.

JOB DESCRIPTION A carefully thought out written description of a job, showing what it involves, how it is to be done, responsibilities, duties, etc. Only when it is known exactly what a job is can one decide (a) how much payment the job is worth; (b) what qualities are needed to do it.

JOB EVALUATION A systematic way of weighing up how much a job is worth in wages or salary, compared with some other job—i.e. establishing a differential between jobs. Must be preceded by a job description.

MANAGER A staff member who has subordinate to himself authorised roles into which he can appoint staff and determine their work; he is accountable for his subordinates work in these roles.

MANPOWER INVENTORY (M.I.) A method of ensuring that a company makes maximum use of its personnel, and that personnel are recognised and promoted as responsible openings occur.

MANPOWER PLANNING (MANNING) The process of filling roles both in the short and long term. In addition to normal replacement due to resignations and retirements, knowledge of how a company will develop over the next few years should show approximately what new types of vacancy, in what numbers, will occur and what present jobs will be redundant. Some idea of the qualifications required for these jobs can be estimated and recruitment planned accordingly.

220

MERIT RATING   A systematic way of estimating how much a man is worth compared with some other man. Factors such as standard of work, time keeping, loyalty, are included.

PRODUCTIVITY BARGAINING   An attempt to obtain a *quid pro quo* for any rise in wage rates. The employer grants a rise in pay only on condition that its total cost is recouped by improvements brought about by a productivity rise, due, for example, to abandonment of excessive overtime, reduction in overmanning, elimination of a restrictive practice.

QUALIFIED MANPOWER   Qualified scientists, engineers and technologists as called for in national surveys of qualified manpower. 'Qualified' implies:
1. A University or C.N.E.E. degree.
2. Corporate membership of a professional institution.

ROLE   A position in a system which is filled by specified means (e.g. election, appointment); every role carries specified responsibility and authority, which are taken on by the person assuming the work.

SALARY PROGRESSION CURVES   As a man gets older his salary usually rises until middle age, then levels off. Plotting the rate of rise against age and comparing one man's graph with another provides a check on whether men of similar abilities are similarly paid.

STAFF   All employees of the company.

SUPERVISOR   A member of the staff who assists his manager by assigning appropriate work to those members of his manager's command allocated to him, and seeing that the work gets done.

TIME SPAN OF DISCRETION   In some jobs a man's supervisor checks on his work every few hours; in other jobs a check is made only every few weeks or months. It is possible to relate salary levels to this time span.

TECHNICIAN   An individual who assists with technical details in a trade or profession: uses tools, instruments and/or special devices to design, illustrate, fabricate, maintain, operate and test objects, materials or equipment: performs mathematical and scientific operations, reporting on and/or carrying out a prescribed action in relation to them: examines and evaluates plans, designs, and data; determines action to be taken on the basis of analysis; assists in determining or interpreting work procedures and maintaining harmonious relations among groups of workers.

PRODUCTION

ASSEMBLY   Two or more piece parts, sub-assemblies or components, put together.
   PIECE PARTS   Single parts, normally manufactured from one material, intended to form part of an assembly, sub-assembly, or component.
   SUB-ASSEMBLY   Two or more piece parts or sub-assemblies put together to be embodied in an assembly or component.

BATCH LOT   A definite quantity of a commodity manufactured by one supplier under conditions of manufacture that are presumed uniform.

JOB CARD   The card on which is entered a record of the time spent on any particular operation or job. In addition, the job card may contain details of the operations to be performend.

LEARNING CURVE   A curve determined empirically, showing the improvement in time that may be expected for each successive repetition of a specific operation or group of operations, whilst an operator is learning the job; such improvement is rapid at first and gradually diminishes, but never fully ceases unless the job is frozen at some given level of productivity. The curve is expressed by the formula:

$$yx^k = c$$

where

y = average time per unit of product from 1 to x

x = total number of units produced

c = time of the first unit

$-k$ = slope of learning curve

When $k = 0.322$, the average time from 1 to $2x$ is 80% of that from 1 to x. This curve works out well for the general run of operations that are not mechanised.

PACKING   Cartons, containers, wrapping materials, etc., and labour involved in packing goods. These may fall into the following categories:

DIRECT PACKING   packing which has a part number and is specifically included in the price.

SPECIAL PACKING   packing not necessarily covered by a part number but called for as a separate item on the contract, or procurement specification, and quoted for separately.

SUB-CONTRACT PACKING   packing carried out by sub-contractors.

OTHER PACKING   protective wrapping, carton or packing case, etc. of unspecified size and quantity which is not covered by a part number and may be recovered as an overhead.

PART NUMBERS   Numbers allocated to all piece part drawings in accordance with a part numbering routine, whether the parts are purchased or manufactured, or whether they are sub-assemblies or final assemblies.

PROCESS SHEET   A detailed exposition of each stage in the manufacturing process, showing sequence of operations, drawings to be referred to, tools, materials, piece parts, time of operation, etc.

PRODUCTION   The last stage in the evolution of a product, involving the actual manufacture and assembly of the product from production drawings.

MODEL SHOP PRODUCTION   products made, usually without tools, by a model shop to meet the initial requirements of the development department and the customer.

PRE-PRODUCTION   products made before the factory is organised for production, to meet initial delivery requirements or confirm production drawings.

SHORT RUN PRODUCTION   a limited production run which is insufficient to make possible a satisfactory level of machine tooling or capacity utilisation.

PILOT PRODUCTION   a limited production run used to test the capability of the production layout, tools, etc., before commencing full scale production.

PRE-SANCTION PRODUCTION   a generic term used where production is started before development is completed.

222

CRASH PRODUCTION a procedure whereby production is permitted in advance of design completion or design approval when delivery of equipment is of paramount importance.

PRODUCTION CONTROL The objective of the production organisation is to meet a delivery programme based either on a sales forecast or a known contractual or customer requirement. To achieve this it is necessary to control materials, labour, and processes. Control systems may, depending on the complexity and number of processes or products, range from the simple to computer operated programmes.

 LINE OF BALANCE (L.O.B.) a technique used in planning and processing batch process, job-shop and, in some cases, line production. The objective of the technique is to try to obtain, and then maintain, a 'balanced' state in the manufacturing system, with the right number of units at the right stages of manufacture at the right time, so that the whole project runs efficiently without hold ups or delays to meet the delivery programme.

PRODUCTION DRAWINGS (OR MANUFACTURING DRAWINGS) Sealed or frozen drawings supported by any necessary process drawings to permit production by a particular agency.

STANDARD PRODUCTS Materials, components or assemblies that are uniform in design, to the company's design or specification; they may be made under licence for another company or under commercial exploitation rights from a Government department, and are manufactured in bulk and sold to a variety of customers.

TIME

 WAITING time when labour is not employed in an activity, due to non-availability of programmed work, materials or facilities.

 QUEUEING the time for which the unit waits for resources i.e., men or machines, to become available.

 SETTING UP the time taken to set up a machine or test equipment for the operation.

 PROCESSING (variable time) the time taken to process a batch.

 ACTUAL the time actually taken to process a unit.

 ALLOWED the time allowed to an operator to process a batch; it may include learning allowance, setting up time, and other allowances.

 ESTIMATED the time estimated for setting up and processing. It usually presupposes a normal operator working at normal speed.

TEST GEAR Equipment acquired for the purpose of testing plant, products or equipment. As this is usually considered to be capital equipment, adequate records must be kept of cost, siting, maintenance, etc.

TOOLS Special equipment made, normally for use on machine tools, to facilitate the manufacture of a piece part.

 SOFT TOOLS temporary tools with a limited life, usually made for the manufacture of prototypes.

WORK STUDY A generic term for those techniques which are used in the examination of human work in all its contexts, and which lead systematically to the investigation of all the factors affecting the efficiency and economy of the situation under review, in order to effect improvement.

 METHOD STUDY the systematic recording and critical examination of existing and proposed ways of doing work, as a means of developing and applying easier and more effective methods and reducing costs.

WORK MEASUREMENT the application of techniques designed to establish the time for a qualified worker to carry out a specified job at a defined level of performance.

TIME STUDY a technique for recording the times and rates of working for the elements of a specified job carried out under specified conditions, and for analysing the data so as to obtain the time necessary for carrying out the job at a defined level of performance.

SYNTHETICS a technique whereby times established for particular operations, or parts of operations, are used to build up the time for a job carried out under specified conditions at a defined level of performance.

PREDETERMINED MOTION TIME SYSTEM (PMTS) a technique whereby times established for basic human motions (classified according to the nature of the motion and the conditions under which it is made) are used to build up a time for a job at a defined level of performance.

ACTIVITY SAMPLING (WORK SAMPLING OR RANDOM OBSERVATION METHOD) a technique in which a large number of instantaneous observations are made over a period of time, of a group of machines, processes or workers.

VALUE ANALYSIS An organised effort at the production stage, directed at analysing the function of systems, equipment and components with the purpose of achieving the required function at the lowest overall cost, consistent with requirements for performance, reliability and maintainability.

BIBLIOGRAPHY

Glossary of Work Study Terms, Organisation for European Economic Co-operation, Paris (1958)
B.S. 3138: 1959, *Glossary of Terms in Work Study*
KENDALL, M. G., BUCKLAND, W. R., *A Dictionary of Statistical Terms*, Oliver and Boyd, 2nd edit. (1960)
HEYEL, C., (Ed.), *The Encyclopedia of Management*, Reinhold, New York (1963)
List of Publications Concerning Management Terminology, International Council for Scientific Management, Geneva (1963)
BOSLEY, D. J., *A Glossary of Commercial Terms*, Blackie (1964)
COMPTON, H. K., *Glossary of Purchasing and Supplies Management*, Purchasing Officers Assn., London (1965)
Encyclopedic Dictionary of Production and Production Control, Prentice-Hall (1965)
Glossary of Terms Relating to Restrictive Business Practices, Organisation for European Economic Co-operation, Geneva (1965)
Glossary of Terms for Quality Control, The Institution of Engineering Inspection (1965)
GREENWALD, D., *et al*, *The McGraw-Hill Dictionary of Modern Economics; a Handbook of Terms and Organisations*, McGraw-Hill, New York (1965)
SELDON, A., PENNANCE, F. G., *Everyman's Dictionary of Economics*, Dent (1965)
GILPIN, A., *Dictionary of Economic Terms*, Butterworth (1966)
Glossary of Terms Used in Research and Development and Supply Procedures, Ministry of Aviation (Central Statistics) (1966)
PERRY, F. E., (Ed.), *Business Terms, Phrases and Abbreviations*, Pitman, 13th edit. (1966)
Terminology of Cost Accountancy, Institute of Cost and Works Accountants, London (1966)
ARGENTI, J., ROPE, C., *Glossary of Management Techniques*, British Institute of Management (1967)
B.S. 4200: 1967, *Guide on the Reliability of Electronic Equipment and Parts therein. Part 2: Terminology*
Glossary of Management Techniques, H.M. Treasury, H.M.S.O. (1967)
HAMBURGER, E., *A Business Dictionary and Vocabulary*, Prentice-Hall (1967)
HANSON, J. L., *Dictionary of Economics and Commerce*, Macdonald & Evans, 2nd edit. (1967)
Management Today, Annual Review, British Institute of Management (1968)

Index

Index

Index